Aquaponics

Raising Fish & Growing an
Abundance of Tasty, Organic
Vegetables – Without the Confusion
& Cycling Problems!

Margaret Fisher

Disclaimer Notice:

Table of Contents

Introduction

Are you fascinated by the idea of trying a new approach to gardening? Tired of scrambling around on sore knees? Maybe you don't have much space in your garden or house. Or possibly, there's a limited water supply where you live. If you can relate to any of the above, aquaponics could be the answer to your problems!

If you've never heard of aquaponics, you are probably not alone. Even if you have heard the word thrown around before, you may not actually know what it is or how it works. Regardless, you have come to the right place. This book will teach you everything you need to know about Aquaponics - from what it is, the advantages it offers over other gardening methods, to how to put together your first aquaponic system. You will discover the ins and outs of the different aquaponic techniques, and you'll be able to choose a system layout that is suited to your garden or home. Furthermore, you'll discover the best breeds of fish to raise and the best plants to grow. You'll become an expert in the science and the bacterial process that drives aquaponics, and you'll learn the most common mistakes that beginners make, so that you can avoid the struggles and the confusion!

Both of my parents were keen gardeners, and I've been around plants for as long as I can remember. My mother always said that I had green fingers – and thumbs! For over ten years, I've been a part-time aquaponics farmer during every spare hour that my day job isn't stealing my time! In that time, I have built countless aquaponic systems, each one not always so successful as the last. Throughout this learning process, I've perfected most of the various techniques. Over the years, I have helped many close family and friends to set up and build new Aquaponic systems, and they've never looked back - not only do they have a fun new hobby, but they also have delicious home-grown produce to show for their time and effort. Now the time has come for me to pass on my wealth of knowledge. I want to shorten the learning curve for you.

Although this book has been written out of my love for Aquaponics, I want to show people that with a little bit of patience and understanding, aquaponic gardening doesn't have to be as tricky as some people make it out to be. Some people struggle to get their heads around the nitrification process, others see the initial set-up as the roadblock, but once you dedicate the time to learn about the processes, they become pretty simple!

In our modern world, there are incredible amounts of overconsumption and waste. Our entire planet is at risk. We need to act now. Aquaponics is one of the most sustainable agricultural farming methods; it uses far less water than traditional gardening techniques and uses no harsh chemicals or fertilizers that can leach into our waterways and pollute the environment.

This book has been written in an easy to read, no-nonsense manner, without complicated jargon, so that even a complete aquaponics novice can make this work. By the end of this book, you will be armed with all the knowledge you need to build, maintain, and operate your Aquaponic system. Within almost no time at all, you'll have your Aquaponic system up and running, cultivating fresh, home-grown vegetables and delicious fish, virtually on autopilot!

So what are you waiting for? Let's get right to it.

Chapter 1 - What Is Aquaponics? And Why Is It Superior?

Before we start, let's get clear on what Aquaponics is, and what makes it work. Aquaponics is a powerful combination of Aquaculture and Hydroponics; it's a unique way of growing plants in water while simultaneously raising fish. Taking full advantage of the Nitrogen Cycle, an Aquaponics system works when nitrifying bacteria break down fish waste into nutrients, that the plants are able to utilize. A pump pushes this nutrient-rich water through a series of pipes, up to the grow beds, where the plants use the nutrients - effectively cleaning the water. The clean water is then carried back around to the fish tank, and the cycle repeats. The fish, plants, and nitrifying bacteria have a harmonious relationship, each one reliant on the others, for the system to operate successfully and fulfill its aim.

Why Aquaponics? It's is a question I get asked an awful lot. Why should one bother with an Aquaponics system when fruit and vegetables can be grown very simply with traditional soil-based gardening? It's a valid question, but there are many advantages to growing aquaponically, compared to growing in soil. Let's take a look at six of the primary advantages below.

1. Firstly, the most obvious one - you get fish too! Not only are the fish fun to take care of, but you can also eat them if you choose, depending on which breed you raise. With soil growing, you don't get any bonus fish to eat!

2. Next, a big one for the environment. Aquaponic gardening utilizes approximately 90% less water than traditional soil-based gardening. Aquaponics is especially good at reducing

water consumption, due to the water being recirculated and continuously reused.

3.   Aquaponics is generally less affected by weeds and doesn't require manual watering or any fertilizing, each of which tends to take up precious time when growing plants in soil.

4.   Back strain! The fish tank in an aquaponic system is most commonly held underneath the plants, so the grow beds are typically at waist height. Thus, the strain on your back and knees is less than when tending to plants in a traditional, soil-based garden.

5.   Plants grown in an Aquaponics system have been found to grow slightly faster compared with those grown using traditional gardening techniques. Research has shown that, on average, plants grown in a soil-less system grow between **30 – 50% faster** than those grown in soil. It is thought that this is down to plant roots receiving additional oxygen from the water. This extra oxygen stimulates root

growth and allows plants to absorb nutrients more efficiently, thus leading to faster growth.

< Gashgari, R et al. (2018). Comparison between Growing Plants in Hydroponic System and Soil Based System. Proceedings of the 4th World Congress on Mechanical, Chemical, and Material Engineering. >

< https://doi.org/10.11159/icmie18.131 >

6.   Aquaponics can also be up to 4-6 times more productive on a square foot basis, as seeds can be packed twice as densely as they can in soil.

Further Benefits!

Aquaponic systems can be adapted to suit your needs. If you only desire to grow food for yourself or your family, then you can set up a small system. Alternatively, if you wanted enough food to sell to and feed a whole community, you could set up a more extensive system. Your only constraint is the amount of space you have available (as well as how much time/money you have). Aquaponics has been used successfully in both home and commercial setups, as well as in research facilities.

Aquaponic vegetables can be grown anywhere. In your back garden, allotment, shed, greenhouse, polytunnel, or indoors. I've even seen systems set up in lounges and people's bedrooms! This means that, even people short on space or who don't have a garden of their own can still grow delicious vegetables, so long as they don't mind the system being in their home. It'd be advisable to check if your loved ones are happy for you to set up an indoor garden first, mind you!

Plants can also, in theory, be grown pretty much all year round, depending on what you choose to grow and where you're growing it. Of course, if you opt to grow outside and therefore rely on sunlight, depending on where you live, there may be some seasonal constraints resulting from the number of daylight hours your plants receive.

Aquaponics vs. Hydroponics

Let's quickly take a look at the similarities between aquaponics and hydroponics. Some people will classify aquaponics as a branch of hydroponics and understandably so. Firstly, they both offer a wider, longer growing season than traditional gardening. If your system is housed inside, assuming you provide the optimum amount of heating and light, plants can, in theory, be grown for longer than the season would typically allow than had you planted them outdoors in soil. This is down to the fact that indoor plants are protected against wind, rainy seasons, extreme heat, and other adverse weather conditions that may otherwise affect their growth. Therefore, both aquaponic and hydroponic systems are capable of producing healthy plants and vegetables all year round in areas where this may usually be impossible!

Plants grown indoors are not so susceptible to weed and insect infestations. Weed seeds are distributed by birds or can be blown around by the wind. Even tools used in general gardening can transfer weeds and harmful insects from one area of the garden to another. That's not to say that aquaponic or hydroponic systems aren't susceptible to insects, but gladly, the risk is significantly decreased.

Scientific studies have also shown that, for plants grown in a water-based system, **the yield** is up to 20-25% greater compared with traditional soil-based gardening. Why is this? It is thought that the yield is higher in a water-based system, because the nutrient level is monitored more carefully and more often than in a soil-based garden. Thus, plants are receiving optimum levels of nutrients, and when the nutrient level becomes too low, the grower adjusts it accordingly. The second reason put forward for higher yields is that, as mentioned above, water-based systems are less susceptible to insects and diseases.

< Gashgari, R et al. (2018). Comparison between Growing Plants in Hydroponic System and Soil Based System. Proceedings of the 4th World Congress on Mechanical, Chemical, and Material Engineering. >

< https://doi.org/10.11159/icmie18.131 >

Differences between aquaponics and hydroponics

There are distinctions between the two water-based methods, the most obvious one, of course, being the introduction of fish as part of an Aquaponics system. This addition means that the grow bed must be at least 12 inches deep in order to accommodate space for the fish to swim in. Whereas, in a hydroponic system, typically, a 6 inch grow bed is deep enough for the roots to spread throughout the water.

In soil-based gardens, pesticides are commonly used to keep weeds and insects at bay, whereas in a hydroponics system, significantly fewer chemicals are used. Of course, the use of harsh chemicals or pesticides is absolutely forbidden in an Aquaponics system due to the adverse health effects these substances would have on the fish.

Once the system is established, Aquaponics requires less monitoring because there is no need to flush out and replace nutrients constantly. In aquaponics, this is a natural process, thanks to the nitrogen cycle. Comparatively, in Hydroponics, the grower must add fertilizer and replace the nutrients in the water on a regular basis to encourage plant growth.

In any aquatic system, it's critical to monitor and measure pH levels closely. You can use any pH meter for this task. A neutral pH is 7.0. Anything below that is acidic, and anything above is alkaline. For Hydroponics, the optimum pH is between 5.5 - 6.0. In an Aquaponic system, fish and bacteria prefer more alkaline conditions, but plants prefer more acidic conditions. Therefore, the overall optimum pH level in an aquaponic system should be neutral or slightly acidic; between 6.50 – 7.0 is preferred. Fish excretions will create a naturally acidic environment, so other than monitoring the levels, you shouldn't need to intervene too often. We'll talk more about pH later.

The financial input required to set up an Aquaponic or Hydroponic system is relatively similar. The main difference is the cost of the fish and the additional growing media for the microbial bacteria, in aquaponics. This extra cost will be dependent upon the price of the fish, the variety/breed you choose, and the number of fish, which in turn is reliant upon which plants you intend to grow, and the size of the system you desire to build.

Once a hydroponic system is built, it is necessary to let the nutrient solution stabilize itself before any plants are added, but this generally only takes a couple of days. An aquaponics system, in comparison, is slower to start-up, and because of the requirements of the fish, it can take anywhere from one to three months for the environment to become stable enough that you can start growing.

The ongoing running costs for both systems differ. Aquaponics is slightly more expensive because it uses more electricity. Electricity is required to run the pump that provides oxygenation and aeration in the water. There is also the additional cost of fish food. Hydroponics, however, requires fertilizer to be purchased regularly, which, of course, isn't free.

An ecosystem is defined as a community of interacting organisms inside an environment. An ecosystem is precisely what Aquaponics is. Fish, microbes, and plants all harmonizing together to create an environment that is symbiotically beneficial for all. Because of this symbiotic relationship between the plants, fish, and bacteria, an aquaponics system is incredibly sustainable. A Hydroponics system cannot be defined as an ecosystem and requires more human intervention.

In Hydroponics, climatic temperatures must be kept reasonably low, around 70F (or 21C), in order to prevent the growth of fungus. Aquaponic systems, on the other hand, are able to operate at higher temperatures of around 82-86F (27-30C) because the fish and the microbes can keep fungus at bay. Both systems are suited to different types of plants. Hydroponics is more suited to plants that have higher nutrient needs because the water solution can be adjusted depending on the plant's needs. Aquaponic systems are better suited to those plants with more straightforward nutrient needs.

Pythium – also known as root rot – is often problematic in Hydroponic systems. and although the lower temperatures and sterile environment can reduce the prevalence, it doesn't eradicate the issue. In Aquaponics, however, the microbes and the resulting strength in immunity in this type of system mean that pythium is almost non-existent. Another tick in the aquaponics box!

The water in a Hydroponic system is rich in fertilizer, so disposing of it down the drain can be harmful to the environment because of the chemicals it may contain. Aquaponics waste-water, by comparison, only contains remaining fish waste that hasn't been broken down by the nitrifying bacteria. Therefore, it is perfectly safe to dispose of down the drain. In fact, some growers instead clear out the additional fish waste and re-use the water for their next grow cycles.

Although both types of soil-less systems have significantly fewer insect problems than traditional gardening, both can suffer from aphids, spider mites, and thrips. Hydroponic growers are able to apply pesticides to reduce infestations, whereas aquaponic growers can't. Pesticides in an aquaponic system would be dangerous to the fish, but we'll discuss what you can do to solve this problem instead, in Chapter 6.

Another point to Hydroponics here I'm afraid, while a mechanical failure can be problematic in either system, it is a more significant concern in Aquaponics, where the water is filtered far more frequently. A mechanical failure would mean excess ammonia and nitrates are allowed to build up in the water, therefore, being detrimental to fish health. You need to know that this isn't too uncommon; moving mechanical parts are prone to failure, as fish waste can clog up the system. It's just part of the game that you have to be prepared for and be ready to fix when it occurs.

Regardless of the last couple of points above, I feel that Aquaponics is superior to Hydroponics for several key reasons. Hydroponic systems have higher running costs and have a lower productivity output. In comparison, once an Aquaponic system is established, it is far cheaper and slightly more productive in terms of growth. Aquaponics, as we've said, makes use of fish waste as the primary nutrient source, and thus the plants and fish produced are organic. No fertilizers or chemicals are needed.

Hydroponic systems, in my opinion, are more time-consuming to maintain because they have to be cleaned regularly. Fertilizers and nutrients have to be replenished on a regular basis. Aquaponic systems are far easier to maintain because the water is re-circulated. The plants will do a lot of the 'water cleaning' for you. Often, the method which people choose is dependent upon the resources they have available and how willing or interested they are in each method. Clearly, as you have purchased this book about Aquaponics, this is the method you are most interested in, and while it can be a steep learning curve at the beginning and there is a lot to learn and discover - I believe that for those who enjoy a challenge and are intrigued by the idea of breeding fish alongside cultivating plants, Aquaponics is definitely the superior choice!

With that, let's put Hydroponics to one side. Hopefully, by now, I have convinced you to the merits of Aquaponics, and so now we'll dedicate our full energy towards it! We'll go into the various types of systems in much more detail in Chapter 3 so that you know exactly how to build your system - but here's just a quick overview of the conventional systems you will likely come across in your journey into the world of aquaponics.

Media Based Aquaponics: This is probably, the best option for complete beginners. It uses an inert medium such as shale or clay pellets. Ammonia is converted into nitrites, and then nitrates via biological filtration. It's suited to growing leafy vegetables, fruit-bearing plants, and herbs.

Deep Water Culture (DWC): This system is often used in larger commercial environments, but can work in your backyard too. Plants are placed in holes on a foam-filled raft, which is then floated on a water channel. This method is often used for growing salad vegetables, such as tomatoes.

Nutrient Film Technique: Nutrient-rich water flows through a PVC pipe, and plants are placed into holes in the pipe. This technique is best suited to plants that require very little structural support, such as strawberries and herbs.

The beauty of Aquaponics is that it is suitable for both commercial growers as well as one-man-band (or woman) growers. A system can be small enough to fit into a small room in your house, or could also thrive outdoors in a garden or allotment. Growing indoors is thought of as a better option by some growers, because it reduces the risk of insect infestation and protects your plants from adverse weather conditions, allowing you to grow plants all year round. Where you locate your Aquaponics system doesn't matter too much, so long as the climate is maintained at the optimum temperature, and plants have the optimum amount of light. Use artificial lighting if growing inside.

Ideally, your plants need four to six hours of good sunlight each day. However, contrary to initial trains of thought, fish *don't* need any sunlight. In fact, sunlight accelerates algae growth inside the tank, and therefore it is better to keep your Aquaponic system out of direct sunlight and provide a light source only for your plants instead. Using an opaque tank is one solution. Light can also incite extremely aggressive breeding behaviour in some species of fish, Tilapia being one example.

Many beginners, or outsiders to aquaponics, might assume that only plants such as Cucumber or Tomatoes can be grown in an Aquaponics system, but at the time of writing, more than 150 plants including vegetables, flowers, herbs and *even* dwarf fruit trees have been successfully grown using Aquaponic systems. Whilst it is not new, it is definitely a method that is growing in popularity amongst modern American families.

The plants you choose to grow will be dependent upon the type of system you opt for, the size of system you set up, and the breed of fish you select. However, if you are setting up an Aquaponics system to consume the plants that you grow, then it only makes sense to produce what you enjoy eating. For instance, it's utterly pointless to grow lots and lots of tomatoes if you don't like their bitter taste (like me!) - unless you plan to sell them, of course!

Chapter 2 - Essential Components & Growing Requirements

Building your first aquaponic system can, at first, seem like quite a daunting prospect to a beginner. In this chapter, I'll break down, in separate lists, the main (primary) and secondary components that you'll need to build your first system. Main components are those defined as ones which are absolutely necessary for every variation of system. The secondary components can be treated like a 'pick and mix,' in that, different systems will require a varying number of the optional components.

1- Plants - The whole aim of Aquaponics is to grow plants sustainably. However, the **plants** in Aquaponic system aren't just living in the system, but instead, they play a large role in running it. Thus, they are classified as a major component, as you might have guessed. The plants act as natural water filters by absorbing nutrients and detoxifying the water. This is a particularly important role because the water is rich in nitrates, which, although great for promoting plant growth, can be incredibly toxic to fish if left to build up to unhealthy levels.

2-   Fish – Regular excretions from fish provide the plants with the essential nutrients needed for growth, so it's safe to say that fish are another essential component. Remember, **fish** are living beings, so Aquaponic growers must maintain the tank with care. Fish are actually an incredibly powerful indicator of the health of the overall system; if the fish are thriving, then the plants likely will be too. Your fish should be carefully selected, as not all breeds of fish are suited to living within an Aquaponics system, and some types of fish may only be suited toward growing certain plants in a system.

3-   Nitrifying Bacteria - The third most important component to any Aquaponics system is **bacteria**; without it, there would be no nitrogen cycle, and therefore no aquaponics system.

If you don't have all three of these present, then you don't have an Aquaponics system. For this reason, these three are always listed as the top three most essential aspects. Let's look at the remaining primary components.

4-   Fish tank - You quite clearly can't keep fish without a **fish tank**, so I am going to list this under the essential components. For a beginner, I always recommend the traditional glass or plexiglass type fish tanks that are used for most home aquariums. They can be more expensive than the alternatives, but the reason I like them is because they are non-corrosive, and you can easily see the fish to check up on their health. Other alternatives include plastic tubs or buckets, plastic amphibian cages, or for larger outdoor systems - large barrels. It truly is a personal preference and often dependent upon what you have to hand, as some people will simply want to use recycled or upcycled materials that they have lying around in their garden shed. Whatever you choose to use should be strong, able to hold water without any leaks, provide fish with ample room to swim around, and should be clean and free from harsh chemicals.

The recommended fish tank size is anywhere between 3-20 gallons. Admittedly, it's quite a broad range. You could go larger than 20 gallons if you have the space and money, but remember, the larger the tank, the larger your grow bed will need to be. The general rule of thumb for grow bed size, is 1-2 square feet of growing space, for each gallon of fish tank water. Let's say that you have a large 20 gallon fish tank; that will hold a lot of fish. If you only had a small grow bed (and so fewer plants) connected to it, there won't be enough bacteria to break down all the fish waste. Likewise, too few fish and large grow beds will result in not enough fish waste to feed all of your plants.

5-   Grow beds - The next item on this list is the **grow beds**. You may come across the term media bed or flood table when browsing online groups and forums, but by and large, these terms are used interchangeably. Some people will refer to a 'grow bed,' meaning the grow media, and 'flood table' to mean the container in which that the media sits. Throughout the remainder of this book, I am going to use the term 'grow bed' to mean the container used to hold the grow bed media, nutrient-rich water, and the plants. Again, some people would class this as a secondary component. However, I personally think that it is essential because even if you use a raft system, you will still need somewhere for the plants to grow, even if you don't use a growing medium. If you don't get the grow beds right, you'll likely find that your plants don't grow very well. A good grow bed will provide your plants with all the space they need to flourish.

In terms of fish tank capacity to number of fish, the general recommendation is 50 square feet of grow bed surface area, per pound of fully grown fish, with eight gallons of water for each pound of fully grown fish. Thus, if you have a sixteen gallon fish tank, you will need two pounds of fish, and 100 square feet of grow bed surface area. A smaller four gallon fish tank, will only need around half a pound of fully grown fish, and 25 square feet of growing area.

In the majority of systems, the grow bed will sit above the fish tank, although some growers prefer the grow bed at the side. Either way, you'll need some form of stand to place the grow bed on. The grow bed should be slightly wider and longer than the fish tank. The container you choose to use for your grow bed must be strong enough to hold the growing medium (if using the media-beds technique) as well as the plants, and the water that's pumped in. Common choices include a plastic tub or plexiglass container, sealed with non-toxic, silicone glue.

Now we've covered the main components of an aquaponic system; let's take a look at the secondary components you might need.

Grow Bed Media: This is the material used in the grow bed; it needs to be suitable for bacteria to thrive, as well as being limestone-free so as not to affect your water's pH level.

Water Pump: This is where the main electrical drain on your system will come from. It's used to circulate the water around the entire system. The size will depend upon the tank exchange rate, number of grow beds, number of fittings, plumbing length, and pump head height. The pump is an integral part of your system. It is so crucial that you select the correct one for your system. If you choose the wrong pump, you could end up with a system that doesn't work as efficiently as possible. In a small system, a submersible pump sat in the fish tank works well;

it will also create 'turbulence,' which increases the dissolved oxygen in the water. In a bigger system (where there is a larger volume of water that needs moving), an inline pump will be needed. Some people also add an additional air pump (aerator) in larger systems to ensure there is adequate dissolved oxygen in the water.

Pipes: Usually made of PVC, pipes transport the water around the various stages of the system. Pipes need to be appropriately sized for the system. It is important to keep them free of any solid waste, which could clog up the pipes, stopping the water from flowing and, in turn, blocking the system.

Aerator: Plant roots need plenty of oxygen, as do the fish; an aerator will constantly aerate the water, providing more dissolved oxygen, which will lead to better fish health and rapid plant growth.

Artificial Lights: Plants require light for photosynthesis, but lights are optional depending upon where you live, the natural climate, and the area in which your system is placed. For example, if you live in a warm country where there is plenty of sunlight and warmth, you may not need lights, whereas if you live in colder climates where there isn't much natural light for most parts of the day, then lights will be essential.

Back-Up Systems: While these are optional, they are definitely recommended. If there is a power failure, your back up system can maintain power, which will not only keep your fish alive and well, but can also stop you from losing everything you've worked so hard for.

A **sump tank** is a low space used for collecting undesirable and waste liquids, and for increasing water volume. Sump tanks are optional depending on the system's design and complexity, but in general, they are more suited towards beginners. Often times, when incorporating a sump tank in your system, bear in mind that your system might not be sophisticated enough to add more plants at a later stage. Therefore, you may end up needing to rearrange various components in your system in order to add another grow bed, if you decided you wanted a bigger system later on. Sump tanks are recommended if you are looking at a Chift Pist style system (see Chapter 3 for more information on the types of systems a sump tank is useful for).

A **filtration system** can be either an active carbon filter or a de-chlorination solution to de-toxify mains water before it enters your fish tank.

Heating Elements: Again, this is optional depending on your natural climate, the types of plants and fish you are using, and your target water temperature.

Timers & Controllers: If you desire to be less hands-on, having timers for lighting, pumping, and various other processes that require intermittent use can be extremely helpful in saving some of your valuable time.

The components listed above are needed to get your system up and running, and in most cases, only need to be purchased at the beginning of your aquaponic journey. The next set of items are those required to manage and maintain your system, and these are all needed, no matter which technique you settle on.

Fish Food: The nutrients in the water will be sufficient to keep your plants happy, but how should you feed your fish? You could use regular pet shop fish food, but many of these can contain ingredients that just aren't suitable for your plants, so I recommended that you find an organic fish feed, just search 'Aquaponic Fish Feed' online and order away!

Seeds: Quite clearly, you won't be able to grow plants unless you start with a seed (or seedlings). To get started, you will need seeds, germination trays, or alternatively, a seed starting kit.

Cycling Kit: This is a very important source of ammonia and nitrifying bacteria that is necessary to start the nitrification cycle and get your system ready before the fish can be safely introduced.

Water Quality Testing Kit: You will need to test your water quality on a regular basis to ensure it is safe for both the plants and the fish. These can be bought from any reputable online Aquaponics store.

pH Monitors & Adjusters: Checking and adjusting the pH in an Aquaponics system is necessary in order to maintain a suitable environment.

Testing & Monitoring Equipment: There are some other variables that you need to test relating to your water, as well as pH levels: these include temperature, dissolved oxygen (DO), and iron levels, to name but a few.

Gardening Supplies: These are easy to forget. You'll need to prune your plants, just like you would if you were growing them in soil. Although you won't need a kneeling mat, you will want to ensure that you have a pair of gardening gloves, spray bottles, pruning shears, and so on, to hand.

Pest Management: You may, at times, find that pests are attacking your plants; if you do, you should only use products that are specific to – and therefore safe for – an Aquaponics system. These need to be free of harsh, synthetic chemicals. Otherwise, they are likely to affect the health of your fish.

Water Quality Parameters.

Being an aquaponic gardener requires a basic knowledge of water chemistry. Let me try to pass on some of what I can still recall, deep in the depths of my memory, from my Chemistry major, all those decades ago!

How often you test your water parameters will be dependent upon what you exactly are testing for, but my advice is that you check the water on a daily basis when you are first setting up your Aquaponics system. By doing this, you can make any necessary adjustments immediately. For example, when beginners are setting up a new system, one problem they tend to come across is the ammonia levels being less-than-ideal. If you make it a habit to test ammonia levels every day, you can pick up on this and adjust it before it gets out of hand. You can do this by either diluting the water, reducing feed quantity, or increasing aeration. Once your system has settled down and is running well, and you are more confident in what you are doing, you can gradually reduce the frequency of your water testing.

One common mistake that I see with people who have just set up their first Aquaponics System is that they check the water parameters regularly, but they don't write anything down! I cannot stress enough how important it is to record the data each time you test it. This will enable you to spot any trends.

'You cannot manage what you do not measure' – Peter Drucker

I would recommend that you keep a designated notebook in which you write down not only the data you take, but also make a note of any alterations you made. Recording these notes each time not only allows you to see if the alterations made had any effect, but if you reencounter the same problem, you can go back and see what you did to solve the problem previously - making it faster to address any future issues.

So what exactly are we testing the water for? The five key water quality parameters are **water purity, pH, cleanliness, Dissolved Oxygen (DO),** and **temperature.**

Water is the lifeblood of the Aquaponics system, and if it isn't of high quality, this will hugely impact the overall functioning of your system, and therefore your results. Before you add any water into your Aquaponics system, it is essential that you test it. One mistake people make is assuming that rainwater is natural and would, therefore, be suitable for an aquaponics system, and while this can be true, it is still vital that you test it. Some areas of the world have overly acidic rainwater, and various forms of pollution, which can have a detrimental effect on an Aquaponics system. Test it!

A good source of water in homes is mains water (tap water), most growers get their water for their Aquaponics system here, but again, it must be tested and treated (if necessary) before being added to the system. Depending upon where you live, tap water is often chemically treated. In the Western World, mains water usually has Chlorine added to kill harmful pathogens and bacteria. High levels of Chlorine, however, can be toxic to your fish as well as your plants. Thus, water needs to be treated first. Chlorine dissipates when it comes into contact with air, so one approach to get rid of the Chlorine is to leave the tap water in an open container and leave it for around 48 hours. Chlorine also dissipates quickly upon aeration of the water.

Chloramine is another common disinfectant found in drinking water. Sadly, however, it is not as easy to remove as Chlorine. If it does happen to be in use in your area, you will need to purchase an *active carbon water filter* or some Sodium Metabisulfite tablets.

There are other chemicals that can be used to treat tap water, but the best practice is to speak to your water supplier. They should be able to provide information on exactly what is in your tap water, so you can test and treat for it accordingly. I cannot stress enough how important it is for you to do this before you add any fish or plants to your Aquaponics system. If you don't get the water purity right, then your system is as good as finished before it has even begun. You may find that you live in a 'hard water' area. Hard water contains high levels of Calcium or Carbonates. Don't worry, though. This is generally safe to use in an Aquaponic system without harming any of the major components. Water that has excessively high salinity should not be used in an Aquaponic system, though.

In the scientific world, pH stands for the 'Power of Hydrogen' and is a measurement of the concentration of Hydrogen ions in a liquid. The more Hydrogen ions there are, the more acidic the solution is – and the lower the pH number. The pH scale ranges from 0-14 with the values of 0-7 being acidic, 7.0 being neutral, and 7-14 being alkaline or basic.

pH is often referred to as the 'master variable' because it affects a wide number of other factors, such as the nitrification of biofilters and the ratio of toxic to non-toxic ammonia. When adjusting the pH, you need to consider the needs of the fish, plants, and bacteria. They all require different pH levels, so the key to a healthy system is finding a happy medium. For instance, the nitrifying bacteria thrive at a pH greater than 7.5. If levels fall below 6.0, then these bacteria will stop working altogether. The pH for fish such as Tilapia should be around 5.0-10.0 (a wide range admittedly), whereas some plants tend to grow better if pH levels are less than 6.5. This is why it is vitally important to plan your system carefully so that you can try to find fish and plants with similar pH needs.

A good compromise is to keep the pH between 6.8-7.0. This is a pretty small range to aim at, so as a beginner, you are likely to find yourself constantly monitoring and making adjustments to make the mark. As a result, for beginners, it's best to aim for a pH between 6.4-7.4 - this should generally satisfy all three components. While it may not provide perfect growth and results, your system should tick over without any detrimental effects. Once you become more skilled at maintaining and adjusting the pH level, you can begin to manipulate it to optimum levels that will promote faster growth!

Again, for a beginner, it is recommended that you test pH on a daily basis. The pH tends to decline naturally due to the nitrification process. If you delay too long between testing, the pH could drop so much that the nitrification process will be significantly reduced or stop altogether, which would cause ammonia to build up to levels that would jeopardize the health of your fish.

If the pH drops below 5.0, a base (scientifically defined as a chemical species that donates electrons), either Calcium Hydroxide or Potassium Hydroxide, should be added to the system to bring the pH back to nearer the 7.0 mark. Add bases gradually over one or two days. PLEASE use Hydroxides with caution as they can burn your skin. A less corrosive alternative would be Calcium Carbonate or Potassium Carbonate. If your pH drops below 6.0 and you live in an area where your mains water has a high calcium content, then sometimes, just adding a little extra water can be sufficient enough to raise your pH level.

What if the pH starts to rise instead? To decrease your pH, acids such as Phosphoric, Nitric, or Muriatic Acid may be used. Phosphoric Acid is the safest option, and the plants will benefit from the extra phosphates that it brings. The downside to Phosphoric Acid is that it can aggravate any existing algae problems; therefore, it may be wise to use one of the other options if you have issues with algae. Please avoid vinegar, it is too weak. Throw out the citric acid too, it's too anti-bacterial; you could end up doing more harm than good. The pH balance can be tricky to maintain at first, but as long as you monitor it regularly and adjust accordingly, you will be just fine.

Next on your list, is **cleanliness**. Solid waste like uneaten food, fish feces, and algae, can all build up quickly and settle at the bottom of the tank. It is recommended that you clear this solid waste regularly to prevent it from entering the biofilters or grow beds. If you aren't strict with this, it can collect at the plant roots and stop them from effectively taking in critical nutrient. As this solid waste decays, it also uses up Dissolved Oxygen (DO). DO is needed by the nitrifying bacteria to convert ammonia and nitrites, then into nitrates - therefore, ammonia levels become too high. Then, not only would solid waste affect the water quality and the health of the plants and fish, but solid waste can also clog your pipes.

Dissolved Oxygen is a measure of the quantity of molecular oxygen present in the water and is measured in milligrams per liter (mg/l) or in parts per million (PPM). DO is critical to the survival of the all-important nitrifying bacteria. Different species of fish require various levels of DO for maximum growth and optimal health. Warm-water fish, for example, Catfish, Bass, and Bluegill, require 5 mg/l, whereas cold-water fish such as Trout require around 6.5 mg/l of DO. Tilapia can tolerate lower DO levels, but their growth rate will be affected if the DO levels get too low, and you might see the Tilapia trying to swim up to the top of the tank toward the oxygen-rich surface water.

Non-ideal dissolved oxygen levels will adversely affect fish, plants, and the nitrifying bacteria and so you need to find a happy medium for each. Usually, this is between 5-8mg/l. At this level, all three components should thrive! While some fish may be satisfied with lower DO levels, it is far safer to maintain a higher level so that you meet the needs of the bacteria and the plants too. Water temperature and DO are also closely linked, in that the warmer the water, the less oxygen it can hold. In warmer climates and during hotter spells during the year, it is crucial to increase aeration to counteract this. It can be a challenge to monitor DO levels in small scale systems because finding a truly accurate DO measuring device can be difficult, and they can be expensive. If you want to take aquaponics really seriously, it's worth investing in one! But if this is just going to be a fun hobby, you can probably live without a DO monitor.

Temperature is another vitally important factor that you need to get right. Warmwater fish such as Bass, Catfish, Tilapia, and Goldfish prefer temperatures of 65-85F (18-29C). Coldwater species like Trout favor temperatures of approximately 55-65F (12-18C). Growth will slow down, reproduction will decrease, and fish may become more susceptible to diseases if the temperature falls outside of the optimum window for each species. Most vegetables thrive at temperatures between 70-75F (21-24C). Water chemistry and water testing may seem complicated, but if you invest in a good water testing kit, then it becomes relatively simple to do these tests. These kits are easy to use and work based on color changes.

Filters

Let's talk about solids for a moment. In an Aquaponic system, you will encounter three different types of solids - floating, settable, and suspended. No matter which technique or system you operate, these solids will inevitably be present at some point in your journey and they'll need to be removed. For <u>raft systems</u>, you will need some sort of filtration system to remove this solid waste, otherwise, this waste will gather in your raft beds and decay, using up the Dissolved Oxygen (DO).

However, for <u>media based techniques</u>, the media bed can act as a filter to remove solids, which can then be broken down by the bacteria (as well as by red worms – you'll learn about Vermiponics in Chapter 8)! Therefore, solids often aren't usually too much of an issue in media based systems. If they are, it is generally for the following reasons;

- Mediocre quality fish food; cheap fish food is not well processed or formulated (hence it's low price), so large chunks of undigested and decaying waste material will pass through the fish and into the water.

- Too much fish food; you may have chosen excellent organic fish food, but if you use too much of it at once, then the leftovers will be left to float in your tank. This is a common issue with Tilapia because they have a 'pass-through digestive system.'
- Overstocking of fish
- The growing medium is too fine; If the medium is overly fine, it can prevent water from flowing through your grow beds, which causes them to clog up. This is why a larger media type is highly recommended and why I wouldn't endorse using pea gravel or sand.

There is often an argument as to whether Aquaponic systems do or don't need filters. For beginners, I would recommend starting with a media based system because it is easier to manage, and you don't have to worry about filtering as much. I would advise you to start out _without_ a filter and see how you go, but it is entirely up to you.

Can I Buy A Complete Aquaponics System?

Thanks to the internet, these days, we can purchase anything we want instantly, at the click of a button, usually with next-day delivery. New growers are often eager to know why they would bother to build their own Aquaponics system, when they could just buy a pre-made one? It's a valid question because building anything from scratch takes time - you need to source materials, find tools, figure out how to build it, and then find the time to put it all together! Regardless of all this, I'm personally not a fan of ready-made Aquaponics systems.

The first reason is the cost. A pre-made system is incredibly, eye wateringly, expensive! It can cost anywhere from 2-10x as much to buy one. It is far cheaper to build your own, and the materials are easy to source when you know where to look. The second reason for not purchasing a ready-made system is that it is beneficial to understand the ins and outs of your system. This way, when something goes wrong, you're more likely to know how to fix it. Furthermore, it can be gratifying to make something yourself and see it up and running, especially something so useful as an Aquaponics system. Finally, designing a system yourself means that you can customize it to suit your needs. A pre-made system won't necessarily fit into the space you want it to fit into, but if you make your own, you can design it so that it looks how you want it to look and so that it fits exactly where you want it to fit.

Chapter 3 - Different Aquaponics Techniques

There are a plethora of different ways to set up an Aquaponics system, but the three main techniques are media filled beds, Deep Water Culture, and Nutrient Film Technique. In this Chapter, we will look at each one in more depth. If you need visual inspiration for any and all of these systems, the best place to go is Reddit. It's FULL of design inspiration – remember, no two systems will ever be built the same! -> www.reddit.com/r/aquaponics/top/?t=year

Media Filled Beds

The most popular technique with both large commercial growers, as well as household hobbyists like you! In a media based system, plants are grown in containers filled with a *media* such as clay pebbles, lava rock, pumice stones, or gravel. The nutrient-filled water from the fish tank is pumped into these beds, and the plants take the essential nutrients from the water before it is drained back into the fish tank. The media serves as a natural filter for solid materials like fish waste (that haven't been broken down), parasites, and other problematic materials. This stops them from returning to the fish tank. The chosen media should be able to hold (but not trap) water and should remain aerated, allowing plants to extract the nutrients more effectively. As mentioned earlier in the book, ensure that the media you choose is not overly fine (like sand).

The big focus for this Aquaponic technique is clearly the grow bed, as this is where the plants will be raised. The standard shape tends to be rectangular, but there are various things to take into consideration when planning your grow beds. For example, they should be strong enough to hold the water, growing media, and plants - and if your system is set up outside, these grow beds should be able to withstand adverse weather conditions. The grow beds should ideally be made of food-grade materials that will not affect the system's pH or transfer any unwanted chemicals into the water. Finally, the grow beds need to be able to connect effectively to the other system components as easily as possible. Otherwise, you may have difficulty plumbing it all together. Not to mention, they must also provide adequate filtration.

Another imperative factor is that your grow beds should be the correct depth and size in relation to the volume of your fish tank. A general rule of thumb is a 1:1 ratio; this, of course, means the volume of your grow bed should be equal to the volume in your fish tank. This isn't a hard and fast rule, other people may state differently, but I think that because it's easy to memorize, it is a good rule for a beginner to keep in mind when they are first setting up an Aquaponic system. For optimal plant growth, grow beds should be around 12 inches in depth in order to be able to successfully cultivate an ecosystem that will be beneficial to your plants.

To give you an idea of how these grow beds
work, we can divide them into different sections;
or what growers usually label as 'zones.'

If we start at the top, the first section is the
surface or the 'dry zone.' The top 1-2 inches (5cm)
serves as a barrier to prevent any light from hitting
the water directly, which could cause fungus to
grow. It also minimizes evaporation and helps to
prevent diseases such as collar rot.

The next section is the root section, which is
pretty much exactly as it sounds in that the roots
grow here - and this is the area that is regularly
flooded and drained (more on that later). The
'flooding' helps to spread nutrients, moisture, and
particles of fish waste amongst the root area,
whilst 'draining' allows the clean water to drain
away completely, in turn enabling oxygen-rich air
to reach the root area.

The final section is the area that collects the
solids, sometimes known as the 'mineralization
zone.' This is typically the last 2 inches (5cm) of
the grow bed. Fish waste, worm castings, and any
other solids will collect here.

A variety of different grow media are suitable for Aquaponic grow beds. I will cover the most popular options here. You may already have an idea of something else that you that wish to use - if this is the case, then please keep in mind that grow media must have a neutral pH, otherwise, the pH in your fish tank will be affected. Limestone is not suitable, and when you are buying any grow media, you need to ensure that it is free from limestone. A vinegar test can determine whether a grow media is suitable before you go ahead and buy it in bulk quantities. To carry out this test, simply place a handful of the media you are considering into a plastic jug or cup, and add ordinary household vinegar. If bubbles appear (i.e., being released from the rock), then it most likely has a high pH, and you should seek to find an alternative. If you are buying from a garden center or somewhere similar, you may feel silly taking a jug of vinegar with you. If you ask the staff, sometimes they will let you take a handful of each media with you so that you can test it at home. It may be advisable to bring some pots or small bags with you so you can take each handful of media home easily.

Whichever grow media you choose, it must be organic and must have an adequate surface area to allow bacteria to grow while allowing water to reach the plant roots easily. I would always advise that whatever media you choose to use, wash it thoroughly before you add it to your grow beds, just to ensure that there are no dangerous particles that could hurt your fish.

Gravel tends to be the most popular as it's often the easiest to find and can often be the least expensive. Gravel is available in different sizes; i.e., for taller plants such as tomatoes, ¾ inch gravel tends to be better than pea gravel, which can get clogged. Equally, ¾ inch gravel may be too heavy for smaller plants, so it is advisable to plan out what you want to grow first and then consider gravel size before you purchase any grow media. Gravel can be rough on your hands when you are maintaining your beds. I've also found that it doesn't always hold water all that efficiently.

Clay pebbles, or Hydroten/LECA (Lightweight Expanded Clay Aggregate) as they are sometimes known, are essentially small balls of clay that have been processed at a very high temperature.

The advantage of clay pebbles is that they are lightweight for you to move around easily, yet heavy enough to support small to medium-sized plants. They tend to be non-degradable, pH neutral, and non-toxic, meaning they are ideal for an Aquaponics system! They are reusable and will last for years. They provide an excellent habitat for microbial colonies. A high pore space means that these clay pebbles cause fewer blockages, and air can move around between the pore spaces allowing oxygen to reach the plant roots.

The downside to this type of media is the price, but in the long term, it can be a better investment because, as stated above, clay pebbles can last for a very long time. Another disadvantage is that some people report that the color from the clay can turn the fish tank water red. As mentioned previously, I would always recommend that you wash any media before adding it to a grow bed anyway, so this could help to reduce the amount of color that washes off into your tank. Pebbles tend to float until they become fully saturated, which means they can get sucked into filters and cause blockages when first introduced. They also don't have great water holding capacity, so when the water is drained, plants may become dry and wilted; this, of course, depends on how needy your plants are for water and the climate in which you live. It's worth keeping in mind, though, as you may need to find a way to keep the media moist during draining.

There are pros and cons to absolutely everything, and Aquaponics is no exception. When choosing a technique or system, it is important to find one that is suitable for you; what I may find works for me won't always suit you. While this is a guide, I think it is important to show you, the reader, both the good points and the bad, so that you can make an informed decision.

Pros of a Media Filled Bed Type System

Inexpensive - I think media filled beds are fairly inexpensive to build in comparison to other systems, but this will be dependent upon what is available in your area and what your budget is. Some people want to build their systems on a shoestring, and others want to splash out on an expensive system that will last them for a lifetime.

Widely suitable - The media filled bed method is suitable for a variety of different plants, from small to medium-sized leafy greens to taller, fruiting plants, like tomatoes. It is also suitable for smaller, household hobbyist systems as well as larger commercial ones.

Minimal Maintenance - While you may need to keep an eye out for any clogging, very minimal cleaning and maintenance is required. The media performs three filtering functions; mechanical, mineralization and, bio-filtration, which breaks down additional waste, preventing it from returning to the fish tank.

Supportive - It can give additional plant support; for example, gravel can be heavy enough to keep plants anchored during light wind.

Aerated - Air can get between the particles, which means plant roots have a good oxygen supply.

Vermiponics Integration - The addition of worms to the gravel bed can help to breakdown fish waste further.

Easy to Adapt to - Media filled beds aren't too dissimilar to traditional soil-based gardening as the grower has something to plant into. It is pretty easy to set up and get used to a media filled grow bed system when coming from a traditional gardening background.

Con's of a Media Filled Bed Type System

Expensive Media - While the system can be deemed reasonably inexpensive in comparison to other systems, this doesn't mean that the media is *dirt* cheap. Get the pun? It can, in fact, be quite expensive. There can often be a compromise between price and quality; I would advise you to spend the extra money to get better quality if possible as, in my experience, the LECA media tends to last longer.

Weight - Media can be heavy, so a robust and rigid structure below will be needed to hold it.

Clogging - Grow beds need cleaning from time to time, and pore spaces in the medium can get clogged with fish waste at times - if this goes unnoticed for too long, it can create unfavorable growing conditions for your plants.

Deep Water Culture (DWC)

This system is also known as the *Raft System* or the *Floating System* and involves growing plants on polystyrene-foam raft boards, which then float on top of the water in the raft bed. Plant roots dangle down into the nutrient-rich water, absorbing large amounts of oxygen and nutrients, leading to rapid growth. For added stability and to stop the plants from falling through the raft holes into the water, net pots are also used.

Many commercial growers use the DWC method because plants grow quickly and with high yields - some also argue that it's a better method for mass production of small leafy vegetables, like lettuce. The nutrient-filled water flows continuously from the fish tank, through the filters, to the raft tank, and finally back to the fish tank. Usually, the raft tank (where the plants are grown) is separate from the fish tank, and the beneficial bacteria can grow in various areas throughout the system.

Particle filters are used to catch solid fish waste, plant material, or anything else that might find its way into the system, which shouldn't be there. It is vital to filter the raft system because solid particles can clog your plant roots, nozzle, piping, or other parts of your system - causing damage and therefore reducing its effectivity. Pumps are used to recirculate water in the DWC system, keeping it moving continually through the system.

Aeration is a fantastic way of adding oxygen to the water using ambient air. This extra oxygen is important for the health and growth of both your fish and plants. There are plenty of options to choose from such as diffusers, air stones, and air pumps.

So what are the advantages of this technique?

Fast Growth - As the roots dangle into the water, they are more greatly exposed to nutrients and oxygen; this means that they tend to grow quicker than in, say, a media filled grow bed.

Ease of use - Raft beds are easy to clean and maintain.

Higher Fish Stocking - Water is continuously pumped around the system, so the water is constantly purified, which means more fish can be stocked in this type of system.

Easy Harvesting - Plants are easier to harvest because their roots are placed directly into the water rather than embedded in any sort of media.

Easy to Build - Fairly easy to set up and possibly the most economical to build, in comparison to other Aquaponic systems.

Spatially Efficient - A highly productive method; rafts can be placed in the tank itself, which means your space can be used more resourcefully.

Highly Stable - The high volume of water in a raft system means the temperature is more stable.

So what are the disadvantages of Deep Water Culture?

Can be Restrictive - It can be restrictive in terms of what can be grown, and growers may find themselves limited to small leafy greens such as lettuce and basil.

Mosquitos! - Depending on the area in which you live, the water can attract mosquitos. Mosquitos can be controlled by using mosquito fish or guppies.

Cycling Issues - It may be difficult to breed the beneficial bacteria because there isn't much surface area for it to grow, compared with other techniques.

Water Evaporation - Water can sometimes evaporate between the raft edges and the tank itself; this means water levels will need to be monitored.

Filtration is Mandatory - The roots are completely immersed in water; therefore, filtration is needed - this process increases costs, and regular filter cleaning is added to your list of regular tasks to carry out. In the next Chapter, you'll find a handy list of daily, weekly and monthly tasks to keep on top of.

Nutrient Film Technique (NFT)

The Nutrient Film Technique is actually a Hydroponic technique that has been adapted for Aquaponics. NFT systems are often used for growing plants with small roots. It is commonly used in commercial operations, but it can be used by hobbyists like you too, though!

This method involves growing plants in long, thin channels. Water continuously flows down these channels to provide the roots of the plants with much needed nutrient-rich water and oxygen. When the water reaches the end of the channel, it flows back to the fish tank via gravity, to the sump tank. If you are using a system that doesn't have a sump tank, then the water will run directly to the fish tank, but bear in mind, the NFT system has to be fitted higher than the fish tank. Like the previous two systems we have looked at, the NFT method uses a water pump. A separate filter is also needed to get rid of any solids, otherwise, these can clog the roots and prevent them from getting adequate oxygen.

In an NFT system, the water will flow from the fish tank through a solid filter, then into a biofilter. Using a *Y-connector*, the water is then pumped in two different directions; some water is pumped directly back into the fish tank, and some is pumped toward the grow channels. The plants will absorb the nutrients, and then the water will flow back to the biofilter, where it is once again pumped into the fish tank or to the grow channels.

An NFT system doesn't have enough surface area to be able to cultivate bacteria; therefore, a biofilter is an incredibly important aspect of this system. Remember, bacteria are needed to convert the ammonia from fish waste into nitrites and then nitrates, which is then consumed by plants. In an NFT system, the biofilter performs this role, and without it, the plants wouldn't have access to the nitrates they need, and the fish could end up living in toxic water. The biofilter is usually just another tank, or a barrel, containing a heavily aerated, porous material. It should be placed after the fish tank and the solid filter, but before the water returns to the grow channels.

The grow channels in this system are usually PVC pipes that are laid out horizontally. The layout of this system can be pretty versatile because it is possible to lay the pipes in various patterns. Thus, you can take advantage of any vertical spaces, fences, walls, or even overhanging balconies! I wouldn't recommend getting overly complicated in the beginning until you have gotten the hang of setting up an NFT system (and running it successfully), otherwise, you could find yourself out of your depth. You can find some great photos online that could give you some ideas, should you feel yourself wanting to be creative with the layout once you think that you ready! Reddit is a goldmine for design inspiration.

Your pipes need to have several holes along the top, and this is where you will place your plants/seedlings. The roots will then dangle into the bottom of the pipe, where the nutrient-rich water shall flow. The water will be pumped from the biofilter into each pipe in an equal flow, allowing plenty of oxygen to reach the roots. The length of the pipes is worth mentioning. Those that are longer than 12 meters aren't recommended because the plants at the beginning of the system will strip the water of nutrients, and the plants at the end, therefore, won't get sufficient amounts. A grow channel that is between 1-12 meters is ideal, although, for beginners, I would recommend using smaller lengths. To allow the water to flow easily, there should be a downward slope of around 0.4 inches over the length of the pipe.

Seedlings are placed into plastic net cups, which are then placed into the holes on the upper side of the grow pipe. You should ensure that the size of your holes matches the size of the net cups.

I would recommend you have approximately 20cm (8 inches) between each plant to provide each one with ample growing space. A common mistake is that new growers excitedly want to plant as much as they can. Thus, they find themselves making the holes closer together because it looks like there is lots of space when planting the seedlings. If you are worried that your seedlings don't have enough support or are not balanced properly, you can add grow media such as clay pebbles or gravel to the net cups around the seedlings.

We will be looking at different plants in more depth in Chapter 6, but as a guide, those which have shallow roots, are fast growing, are lightweight and need less care are all suitable for NFT systems. Root vegetables and those which grow tall, spread, or produce heavy fruit should be avoided at all costs, as there simply isn't enough space or support in an NFT system for these plants to do well. For example, avoid melons, cucumbers, carrots, squash, corn as well as any type of tree. Some plants that need extra care and support can still grow successfully in this type of system - for instance, strawberries, tomatoes, peppers, and a few varieties of eggplant.

The key to success is to plan, plan, and plan some more! Another tip is to monitor the temperature regularly. I mentioned earlier that the water can be susceptible to temperature changes, and because the roots are exposed - they are affected by the water temperature and the natural climate you live in. Plan where you are going to place your system; direct sunlight will not only mean that temperature changes fluctuate dramatically, but your roots could also be exposed to light, which in turn can cause unwanted algae growth.

Maintenance is important; the water pump and biofilter are essential components here. If either one of them stops working, you could end up losing all of your plants or killing your fish. Keep an eye on water flow - often in NFT systems, the roots can partially block the grow channels, stopping water from running through.

What are the Pros of the NFT technique?

Constant water flow - A constant flow of water in the system ensures that the plants always have nutrient-rich water available. This also leads to a low risk of fungal growth and helps to prevent solids from building up on or around the roots.

Root Exposure - The roots are exposed and thus receive plenty of oxygen, which can help to prevent root rot.

What are the Cons of the NFT technique?

Limited Growing Options - Types of plants you can grow in this system can be quite limited because although small vegetables and leafy greens do well, larger plants, with more extensive root systems, simply do not thrive in an NFT system.

Channel Blocking - Because the roots are dangling into the water, as the plants grow, the roots can start to block the channels, so whilst the first few plants in the pipe might receive enough water, those further down the line may not, which may lead to nutritional deficiencies.

Pump Failures - Pump failures are disastrous! Due to the continuous nature of the water flow -

without the pump, the plants won't receive any water and will quickly wilt and die.

For all of these reasons above, an NFT system isn't really recommended for beginners. I believe that it can be a fascinating system if you are more experienced in Aquaponics and want to try your hand at something different, although a beginner may find it easier to start with the media filled bed technique. Equally, however, there isn't technically a right or wrong technique to choose in Aquaponics, and really, the one you select is down to your preference, how confident you feel, and the space you have available. You could even use a hybrid system, combining multiple techniques into one system, as you see fit.

Whichever system you choose, you'll gradually become more successful with it through trial and error - so don't be frightened to experiment. Aquaponics should be – and is – lots of fun! You will always come across difficulties, especially when you're new. Even growers who have been using Aquaponic systems for years can still come across issues. The only difference is how you choose to deal with these issues. Pretty much any difficulty can be overcome, as long as you don't panic, plan your system correctly, carry out regular maintenance and monitoring, and keep learning as you go!

CHIFT PIST

The name 'CHIFT PIST' is an acronym of Constant Height In Fish Tank, Pump In Sump Tank. And no, I didn't think it was a very catchy name either, but never mind! The Chift Pist is very popular with hobbyists. Water from the sump is pumped into the fish tank. The water level rises before it flows out into the grow beds. Water drains from the grow bed into the sump tank before being pumped back to the fish tank. The grow bed can be constantly flooded, or you can add an 'auto-siphon' within the grow bed, to flood and drain it.

Usually, a CHIFT PIST type of system will also incorporate a Solid Lift Overflow (SLO), where that the overflow pipe runs all the way to the bottom of the fish tank, drawing solids up from the bottom, and depositing them into the grow bed. A pump timer isn't needed unless the sump tank is so large that it requires a large capacity of water to top up the fish tank.

One advantage of this type of system is that the water level in the fish tank remains constant, causing less stress for your fish, and the pump in the sump tank is positioned away from fish waste, so there's less risk of blockages.

Flood and Drain

The next type of system we'll look at is a **simple flood and drain**, otherwise referred to as *ebb and flow*. In my honest opinion, I think this is the easiest variation to build and understand. You have a couple of choices with this method. You can either use a standpipe in the grow bed and a timer on the pump, or you can put a siphon in the grow bed, instead. Both work well.

In a flood and drain system, the grow bed is situated above the fish tank. Water is pumped from the fish tank, which then, as the name suggests, floods the grow beds. Nearly all of the media is submerged at this point. The pump will either have a timer or the water will drain back to the fish tank when a siphon in the grow bed is triggered. The way the siphon works is that if there is no timer on the pump, water will still be pumped into the grow bed - but when the siphon kicks in, it takes water out faster than the pump is sending it in. Thus the water level will go up and down. Once the system is set up, it can run almost entirely by itself, without much input.

This design is easy to build and maintain. It is ideal for taller fish tanks, and there is no need for a sump tank. It can be customizable to your needs, and you can set how high you want the water level to be in the grow beds. The downside is that the pump is inside the fish tank, so the water level in this tank can fluctuate a little, which could cause stress to your fish. Additionally, if you live in a hot climate, you have to allow for evaporation of your water, so you may end up finding that your fish tank loses quite a lot of water at times.

Continuous flood, or **continuous flow**, are popular setups too. A continuous flood system involves keeping the grow bed flooded so that the plants are constantly underwater rather than having periods of draining. You can predetermine the height of the water, and a standpipe will be introduced into the grow bed. On the other hand, a continuous flow system has water continually flowing over the roots while moving through the system, as opposed to flooding the entire bed and having the grow bed media actually underwater.

Both setups are fairly similar to the CHIFT PIST method, but rather than specifying when the water is sent back to the fish tank and draining the beds; the grow beds always have a continuous supply of water. This means that plant roots grow into the water and take all the nutrients they require.

A drawback of the continuous flood method is that you can sometimes have trouble with oxygen getting to the roots - unless you have a highly aerated system. A continuous flow system, however, allows roots to get oxygen easily. It's is a nice easy system to run because you don't have to worry about high water levels (although in a continuous flood system, the water level can be lowered by adjusting the height of the standpipe). Moreover, you don't have to worry about timers, which are prone to rare, but occasional failure.

Barrel-ponics

Barrel-ponics is another technique under the Aquaponics umbrella. The theory is the same - fish, plants, and nitrifying bacteria living harmoniously together – but the beauty of barrel-ponics is that is has made Aquaponics extremely accessible for those people who wanted to dabble in this type of gardening, but didn't have much space or money to do so. Barrel-ponics is a cheaper alternative, and even if you only had a small balcony, instead of a large garden, you could still set one up -because you only need a single 55 gallon drum. If you don't mind the less pleasing aesthetics, you could even set one up inside! This type of system is also incredibly popular in areas that are lacking much soil or water.

The system components are pretty much the same as any Aquaponic system, as in, you need a grow bed with media for the plants and a barrel for the fish. As I mentioned, 55 gallons would be big enough, but a larger unit would obviously hold more water and, more water, means more plants can be grown. The grow bed is placed on top of the barrel and needs to be wider than the drum. The type of fish recommended for barrel-ponics are goldfish. Goldfish can live for up to forty years and don't need as much space as other fish, plus they're not affected by cold spells. Of course, this means you won't be able to eat your fish, so this can be a downside for some.

A water pump takes the water from the fish tank, up to the grow bed, and back again, using gravity. Water tubing or pipes will need to form a circle, leading from your water pump outlet to the top of your grow bed. An air pump is required in order to supply air to both fish and plants, whilst an air stone at the bottom of the tank will break up the stream of bubbles from the air pump to increase water oxygenation. The two are joined together by an air tube.

If you can get blue barrels, these are ideal because they don't get so much algae growth, and as long as they are clean and food-grade quality, they are safe for both your plants and your fish. I have, however, seen people using wooden barrels successfully, so it is worth doing further research if you can't get hold of blue barrels but are interested in this type of system. There are two barrel-ponic designs at the time of writing; *chop and flip*; and *split* barrels…

The chop and flip is simple, cheaper, easy to build, and uses only one barrel. The build requires no need for expensive power tools. The split barrel system, however, is a little bit more time consuming and complicated to design and build, as it uses three or more barrels, plus an IBC tote. As a result, it's more expensive.

I have a soft-spot for barrel-ponics because it's genuinely easy and saves on space. Several barrels can give you plenty of grow bed space for a variety of plants. Some people are put off because they want to breed fish which they can eat, rather than goldfish. Bear in mind that this book is aimed at beginners, and my recommendations are based on what has worked best for me. It doesn't necessarily mean that you can't use other fish, but you will need to experiment, and your system may not run at its optimum level until you perfect it!

If you are enjoying reading the book so far, please consider leaving a positive five-star review on Amazon. It will mean a lot to me to see that you are learning a lot from my book, since I spent so much time planning, writing, re-writing, editing, and then editing it again!

Chapter 4 - Building & Operating Your New System

Before you set up your Aquaponics system, there are some things you need to consider carefully. Firstly, where will your system be located? It is key to choose your location *before* you start building. Aquaponic systems can be incredibly heavy, even small ones, and so, it would be wise to put it together in its final location if possible, rather than putting the system together elsewhere and having to transport it once built.

Another reason for choosing the location first, is to take advantage of all the available space. When considering special requirements, you may, in fact, decide that you have room for a bigger system, but want to start with a smaller one, and you could add extra grow beds and fish tanks further down the line.

Will your system be indoors or outdoors? Indoor systems tend to be built slightly differently to outdoor ones, and different materials are often used. For example, you may want to use a barrel for your fish tank outdoors, whereas inside, you might choose a glass tank that looks smarter and fits in better with your décor! Indoors, you'll also most likely want your grow bed directly above your fish tank, rather than to the side, in order to save space. The weight of your system is also an important consideration, especially when building indoors. You wouldn't want to build it on the second floor of your house, only to walk in one day and find it's landed in your lounge! Indoor systems will also require grow lights, so think carefully about where best to build your aquaponic system.

If you opt for an outdoor build, the ground beneath the system needs to be stable and level. Moreover, because these systems are heavy, if you place it on dry or soft soil, the legs of your system could sink, which can lead to flooding. Concrete slabs are a good base for your system. If you do place your system on grass or soil, concrete or wood under each leg may prevent it from sinking. It is recommended that the fish tank is placed on a base to protect it, and to allow for plumbing and drains to be connected underneath.

When choosing the location for your system, you must consider the access to utilities and electrical sockets for your air and water pumps. Inside, this won't generally be an issue. No matter where your system is, remember, water and electricity don't mix well, so all electrical outlets need to be shielded from water. Ensure that you have purchased a residual-current device (RCD), too. You should also consider ease of access. The system will need daily testing and monitoring, and you will, ideally, need to be able to move around the entirety of it to check for leaks, inspect your plants for insects and check up on the health of your fish. Another consideration is the water source you are using; is your system near enough to a water source so that you can top it up with ease whenever necessary? Where will any wastewater be disposed of? Your system also needs to be in a safe location where it won't get vandalized, or attacked by larger animals such as rabbits or foxes - you may want to put a fence around it to minimize these risks.

The final consideration is the climate in which you live. If the weather tends to be hot all year round, then your system will be fine outdoors. If you have harsh winters, will you not operate it during colder months, or will you place your system in a greenhouse all year round? What are your night-time temperatures like? Will you need a heater at certain times of the day? Extreme environmental conditions shouldn't be taken lightly because they can seriously affect your plants. Snow and heavy rain can cause damage to the system too; for instance, large amounts of rain can dilute the water and even flood the system if you have no overflow mechanism. Rain poses a significant danger to unprotected electrical sockets too. Therefore, it would be smart to protect your system (climate dependent) with some sort of shelter – a greenhouse or shed, possibly. Alternatively, you may want to shut your system down when you know that the rainy or cold season is coming, or move it inside.

It isn't just cold weather that can have an adverse effect on your system; you will also need to consider sunlight vs. shade. Sunlight is quite clearly vital for plants, and they'll need to receive the optimum amount of sunshine each day. Equally, if the sun is too intense, you may need to consider some sort of shade system over the grow beds. For instance, lettuce, cabbages, and salad greens don't thrive in the presence of excessive sun and will flourish better in a shaded area. Other plants can show a slow growth rate if they don't receive enough sunlight hours. Consider where, and when, shadows will cross your grow bed location and arrange your plants accordingly; for example, tall, sun-worshipping plants could be cleverly used to shade low-lying, shade-loving plants.

A greenhouse isn't essential for a home Aquaponic system, but having one can be a solution to many problems. For instance, it can extend the growing period or even allow for year-round production of plants in some areas. A greenhouse will protect the system from elements such as rain, snow, and wind, as well as providing protection from pests, predators, and vandals. Working in them is also comfortable during cooler periods. The frame of the greenhouse can also be useful to encourage plants to climb, or can be used to hang up shading material. However perfect a greenhouse sounds, there are some downsides; for instance, depending on how sophisticated you want your greenhouse to be, the initial purchase cost can be pretty steep.

However, this is where things can get complex and can seem overwhelming for a beginner in aquaponics. The thing is, your plants are not the only thing to take into account; you also need to remember that fish are a key part of your system. The fish tank shouldn't receive direct sunlight and should be placed in the shade. Excessive light causes algae growth (due to photosynthesis). Light also acts as a cue to breed, which can turn some fish species, extremely aggressive. Not ideal. Some growers cover their fish tanks with a removable cover. In addition, try not to place your tank under any overhanging trees, which may drop leaves and other debris into your fish tank, affecting your water chemistry, clogging your pipes, and putting your system at risk of contamination. You also need to be wary of predators! Some may see your fish as a free lunch, so some sort of screening will be needed to protect them.

In Chapters 5 & 6, we'll cover the ins and outs of plants and fish in vast detail - so that you don't miss a trick. It would be devastating to build a fantastic Aquaponics system, only to find that your fish aren't happy, and the plants you want to grow aren't suitable.

There is a close relationship between the size of the grow bed and the size of the fish tank. The quantity of fish excretions dictates how many plants can grow; too many fish, or too much fish food - will result in too much ammonia being produced. If, in this case, the grow bed isn't big enough, there won't be enough bacteria to break this waste down fast enough, and slowly the water will poison your fish. Too few fish, and too many plants, will mean there won't be enough nutrients for all the plants to flourish. Like in all aspects of life, balance is key.

Connecting Up Your System

Whichever type of system you decide on using, it will require various PVC pipes, PVC connections, fittings, tubes, and hoses to create the means for the water to flow throughout the system. You will also need some sort of sealant. Usually, the PVC parts are permanently connected using PVC cement, or they can be temporarily sealed using silicone sealant - assuming the joints aren't under excessively high water pressure. As well as the plumbing components, you will also need tools such as hand saws, hammers, drills, electric saws, pliers, screwdrivers, tape measures, and so on. The pipes and plumbing materials used in your system need to be free from toxins, and any plastic should be food-grade to prevent your system from being contaminated with chemicals. Crucially, all pipes should be black or non-transparent, otherwise, algae may start to grow inside.

In Aquaponics, the sump tank is generally placed lower than your fish tank, and this is where all the equipment needed to keep your fish healthy will be placed; filters, heaters, and so on. To simplify, a pump will force water from the sump tank into the fish tank. As the fish tank fills up, the water flows into the grow beds and later drains back into the sump, before being pumped back up towards the fish tank - continuing the cycle.

To simplify the setup and to avoid having to have a complicated network of pipes (and to reduce the risk of pump failure), a 'Bell Siphon' is often used. With the siphon in place, when the water reaches a certain height, it drains out through the siphon *faster* than the rate at which the water fills the grow bed. As the siphon drains the water, holes at the bottom cause the siphon to break the suction, and the whole process begins again.

How it works:

- Water from the fish tank flows into the grow bed, providing the plants with nutrients.
- The water reaches the high mark of the bell siphon and starts to drain into the pipe, causing a vacuum effect, drawing air into the drain pipe too.
- With the air removed from the bell siphon, the water flow via the drain increases dramatically, thus water is draining from the grow bed faster than it is being replenished.
- The siphon eventually reaches the bottom of the grow bed and starts to suck in air instead of water, which in turn causes the siphon to break, stopping the grow bed from draining, and the cycle begins again.

While bell siphons can be tricky to get right, once you have them working properly, they can be extremely effective.

I'm not going to go into too much more detail with plumbing and connecting your system, as it can be difficult to describe. You will be better placed to select which Aquaponics technique you are going to use, then look at some videos online to help you design your system. The actual ins and outs of how to connect it, depends on the size, shape, and set up of your system, which will all be unique to you.

Cycling

No, I'm not talking about getting your bike out here; system cycling is the term given to the process of first establishing the beneficial bacteria for your system, which is, as you know, critical for the nitrogen cycle and therefore your entire aquaponic garden.

Cycling begins when you first introduce ammonia into your system. You can do this by adding every-day, household cleaning ammonia, but please only use the pure kind; avoid anything that contains soap, perfumes, colorants, or any other type of additive. The bottle should list the ingredients or will be labeled 100% ammonia, pure ammonia, clear ammonia, or pure ammonium hydroxide. If it doesn't have one of these terms, don't use it. A novel way to find out if it is suitable is to shake the bottle - if it foams, it isn't suitable.

Pure ammonia can be purchased in DIY stores, cleaning supply shops, or in supermarkets. If you can't find it locally, you can buy it online. There are other sources of ammonia, and these include Ammonium Chloride, human urine, or even a piece of dead fish! Those last two sources are purely for entertainment purposes, and should NOT be added to your system for obvious reasons. ☺

Whichever source of ammonia you use, add it to your fish tank, then start testing the water until you get an ammonia reading between 2 & 4 ppm. If you have a smaller tank, add only half a teaspoon or less, wait, test, then, if necessary, add more. It usually takes around 5 teaspoons of 100% clear ammonia or half a teaspoon of ammonium chloride powder to give you a reading of approximately 3-4 ppm in 100 gallons of water. If you do add too much, you can drain some of the water, and top it back up with new water, then test it again.

One mistake I see newbies making regularly - is adding ammonia, not seeing an immediate reading, then proceeding to add more. The test still reads zero ammonia, so they add more, then they complain the test doesn't work. If you have a reading of zero ammonia, you may have added too much and actually overwhelmed the system. Start again, dilute with fresh water, and take another reading.

Once you get the optimum ammonia reading, you will need to test your water for ammonia, pH levels, and nitrites every day. I recommend you record these, along with notes, so that you can track any changes. At this point, the pH needs to be between 7.0-7.8. A level higher than this is okay during cycling, assuming that you haven't planted anything yet. Equally, though, I would recommend you try to reduce it, just so that you know how to do it – refer back to Chapter 2 for clarity on how to raise and lower pH.

Once the ammonia levels begin to drop, this is a great sign; this means the nitrifying bacteria are starting to convert the ammonia into nitrites, then into nitrates. Add a small amount more ammonia in to raise the levels back to the 2-4ppm range. Record the nitrate levels, too, as this is the next step in the cycling process.

Your system will be fully cycled once nitrite AND ammonia levels fall to (or close to) zero. Once this has happened, you are ready to add the fish; you will no longer need to add more ammonia because the bacteria will start to be fed via the ammonia excreted from the fish and the fish waste! Take a second to be proud and reflect on how far you have come already.

You are almost ready to start planting seeds too. At this stage, the pH should be between 6.5-7.0, because remember, the plants require a lower pH than bacteria. The entire cycling process can take anywhere from 10 days to 2 or 3 months.

Inoculation

Some growers choose to accelerate the cycling process by inoculating the system. There are a number of strategies here...

- Inoculating with store-bought inoculant bacteria at start-up – it costs between $30 - $50, but can save you potentially months of cycling time!

- Taking "inoculator plants" from another aquaponics system and adding them to your system – one problem is that you may bring with it - other things from the donor aquaponic system, like duckweed, crawfish eggs, etc.

- Adding a water sample of media from another aquaponic system or body of water, and adding it to your fish tank. This is sometimes referred to as 'live water'.

The only difficulty with inoculation is that you need to be confident that the source the bacteria is coming from, is a healthy one. You may know somebody who has an Aquaponics system, or you may not. There is always the off chance that you could borrow water/plants from a grower who has diseased fish in their tank without realizing it. By doing this, you would run the risk of introducing disease to your brand new, clean system! Not ideal.

This method of cycling is known as fish-less cycling. The advantage of starting up your system without adding the fish has some benefits for beginners. Firstly, it is far less stressful for both you and the fish! You are not needing to worry about killing off some of your new fish friends while getting the ammonia levels correct. Second, you don't have to worry too much about pH levels, as you don't yet have any fish or plants.

Cycling is far quicker without fish because you can elevate the ammonia concentration to a far higher level than you would if you had fish. If you have fish in the system when you start it up, it can take 4-8 weeks for it to cycle.

In addition, you can control precisely how much ammonia is in your system; if the ammonia level is high, you can stop adding ammonia for a couple of days and wait for the bacteria to grow and nitrites to be introduced. Or, you could remove some water out and dilute with fresh water. It's hard to do this when you have fish in the water because this may throw off the temperature levels.

Once the cycling process has completed, you should add all your fish at once, as opposed to adding them gradually. If using carnivorous or aggressive fish, this can be better because they are far less likely to attack each other if they are introduced together; sometimes, they can be territorial if a number of them are introduced at a later date. For more detailed information regarding fish, don't fear, because Chapter 5 is up next!

Finally, you are ready to plant your seeds. Surprisingly, it is advisable that you start with *seedlings* when your system is first up and running. Once you have plants established and your system has been running successfully for at least three months or more, then you can start adding seeds as well. For more information on plants and seeds, see Chapter 6.

Chapter 5 - Choosing Your Fish

For many Aquaponic hobbyists, this can be one of the most exciting aspects - choosing the fish that you'll raise. You have almost a limitless possibility here. You're able to control almost all aspects of their habitat, such as temperature, space, water quality, food, and so on. Of course, not all fish will thrive in an Aquaponic system, so there are some things you need to consider carefully.

If you are building your Aquaponics system indoors, then you are likely going to have considerably less space than if you were building it outside, in your garden. Contrary to popular belief, the fish usually only occupy around 20-30% of the tank; plants and their roots take up far more space. If you have limited space, it would be wise to choose fish that are small, even when they reach maturity. If your system is inside, you may opt for fish that are ornamental rather than edible. For example, you might not want to look at a tank full of Trout while you are settling down to watch your favorite TV show! In this situation, a tank full of freshwater tropical fish like Neon Tetra, or even Goldfish, would be a better option - but of course, this depends on what exactly you want to keep your fish for, which brings me nicely on to my next point.

To many, having an available supply of fresh, organic fish is tempting. To others, fish are beautiful creatures with their own personalities and are therefore considered pets. I have friends with aquaponic systems who have never even considered that eating their fish was an option. Ask yourself, would you be happy to eat something that you have cared for and looked after for a number of months? I tend to find that people who keep their fish indoors are more likely to see them as pets than those whose systems are outside. On the other side of the coin, fish keeping can become quite addictive, and if you end up with a large system a few years down the line, or if you breed your fish (whether accidentally or on purpose), you may find that you have to take some out. At this point, you can either move them to another tank, but if you enjoy eating fish, there is something quite rewarding about taking a few from your system every now and then, for a fish dinner. This is a decision you will need to make at the beginning. If you have chosen Aquaponics so that you can cultivate fish as well as plants, then you may prefer a system outside which you can stock with edible fish. If you want a functional system, but also an ornamental feature indoors, then you will likely choose more attractive, tropical fish.

The cost will be another factor; smaller fish tend to eat more food than larger fish, and so they can be more costly to keep than bigger fish. Sometimes your choices are limited by the type of fish you have available in your area. It's better to buy local, to avoid the fish being too stressed during lengthy transport journeys. It is essential that your fish are disease-free, otherwise, they will be detrimental to your whole system. My advice is to only purchase from registered fish farms. It would also be wise, if you want to eat the fish, to buy ones that you can breed easily yourself, so that you can replenish your stock easily.

So what are the best type of fish? Below is a list of species that are known to thrive in Aquaponics systems.

Trout

Trout are a fish farming favorite. Most trout live in freshwater lakes and rivers for their entire lives. Others will live out at sea for two or three years and then return to freshwater to spawn. For an Aquaponic system, you can choose from Rainbow, Brook or Brown, with Rainbow Trout being the hardiest.

These fish are carnivorous: in the wild, they primarily feed on other fish and soft-bodied aquatic invertebrates, such as flies and dragonflies, or shrimp.

Trout are edible, although some people complain that they are bony. It is worth keeping in mind that their diet heavily influences their flavor.

- A large tank is required; Trout can grow to about 15 inches within nine months
- Temperature: Trout are cold-water fish, they thrive in temperatures approximately 55-65F (12-18C)
- pH: between 6.7 and 7.7
- Oxygen level: minimum 5.5ml/L

Goldfish

These are great in an Aquaponic system because not only are they a fairly hardy species, but they also produce large amounts of excretions, providing plants with plenty of nitrites and nitrates.

There are two types of species that you can choose from; single-tailed or twin-tailed. It is not recommended that you mix the two because the single-tailed goldfish are faster swimmers, have slimmer bodies and tend to be more aggressive, making it difficult for the twin-tailed species to compete and survive.

- Goldfish are inedible and are best suited for those who want ornamental fish

- Temperature: Goldfish thrive in temperatures between approximately 65-75F (18-25C)
- Rapid changes in temperature can be fatal, so levels must be monitored closely.
- pH: 6.5-8.0

Koi

Koi are another popular choice of aquaponic fish due to their long lifespans. They are adaptable and tend to flourish and breed well within Aquaponic systems. They tend to be fairly resistant to disease and parasites. This makes Koi an ideal choice for beginners.

These fish are omnivorous and will eat just about anything, including plant matter and debris that may fall into their tank, plus any algae that may grow. However, the downside is they are ornamental and not suitable for eating.

- Temperature: 65-78F (18-25C)
- pH: 6.5-8.0

Carp

Carp are oily freshwater fish, native to Asia. There are various types, and they're closely related to Koi, although most people – like me – consider them as separate species. They are a popular choice because they, too, are adaptable, resilient, and are strong breeders.

- Temperature: approximately 80-82F (26-28C)
- pH: 7.5-8.0

Crappie

Crappies are part of the sunfish family and can be found in two varieties - black and white.

They make an excellent species for Aquaponics because they are surprisingly hardy and can tolerate wide temperature changes. This makes Crappies suitable for beginners in one way, because you don't have to be as accurate with your temperatures. However, because they need precise pH levels, this makes them slightly more difficult to keep unless you monitor and adjust pH regularly – which you should actually be doing anyway, by the way.

- Crappie can be eaten, taste great and should grow to a suitable harvesting size of 1lb within two years. The downside to Crappies, is

that they cannot be kept together with other types of fish
- Temperature: 55-80F (12-26C)
- pH: 6.5-8.2

Catfish

These fish do well in an Aquaponics system, because they can tolerate higher stocking density, and are not territorial. They are easy to breed and they grow quickly, making them a fantastic choice for beginners. In fact, catfish are top of my list.

These fish are omnivorous bottom feeders and scavengers. Catfish are ideal for those who want to eat the fish that they raise, as within 3 months they can be ready to harvest.

- Within 12 months they can weigh around 2-3lbs
- Temperature: Approximately 75-85F (23-29C)
- pH range: 7-8

Bass

There are a variety of species of Bass to choose from; Largemouth Bass, the Smallmouth, the Australian or the Hybrid Striped Bass.

Bass tend to be very hardy, so they can tolerate low water temperatures. They have great growth potential and an adult bass can weigh around 12lbs after 16 months. Due to this, they require large tanks.

They dislike bright light and require a strict feeding schedule consisting of small insects and shrimps for babies, with the mature bass eating crayfish and snails. They also eat larvae, worms and high protein pellets. They prefer food that stays on the surface or that sinks slowly, as they don't like feeding from the bottom of the tank. While they are popular in Aquaponics, they are not recommended for beginners as they can be quite 'high maintenance.'

- Bass are edible and can be very rewarding for those who are using their Aquaponics system for the purpose of eating their fish
- Temperatures: Approximately 65-75F (18-24C)
- pH: 6.5-8.5

Tilapia

These are considered to be one of the oldest,

most farmed fish, on the entire planet. They first originated in Africa, in the Nile River Basin of Lower Egypt. They are popular in America, but may be difficult to source for those readers in the UK & Europe.

Tilapia are one of the easiest fish to keep; they are durable, have a fast growth rate, are resistant to parasites, and can tolerate a wide range of water qualities and temperature variations. They're also prolific breeders and can spawn every 4-6 weeks. For all these reasons, they are great for beginners.

They are great for those who want to eat their fish, due to their rapid growth rate, large size, high protein content, and taste. They can reach up to 2.5lbs within 7 months. Some people say they 'taste like mud', which I think is quite unfair - their taste is affected by their food source, and if they live in poorly filtered environments, they won't taste so good. On the flip side, if they are raised in a clean and stable environment and are fed high-quality food, they can be delicious.

Unfortunately, they can become quite friendly with the person feeding them, so much so that you may not have the heart to eat them once they're big enough! Another downside to Tilapia is that they can end up overloading the tank due to the speed at which they breed. This problem can be overcome by purchasing a second tank if you have the space and the resources.

- Temperature: Approximately 70-80F (21-25C)
- pH: 7-8

Jade Perch

An Australian fish, who's popularity in Aquaponics is growing. They can be difficult to source in the US and in Europe, but as Aquaponics is becoming more and more popular, you may be able to source some from a local aquaponic farmer, or else, somebody who is breeding them, therefore I have included it here regardless.

They are great fish for Aquaponics because of their growth rate, hardiness, and nutrition. If you feed them food high in Omega 3, they'll retain this, giving you a highly nutritious meal.

- A downside is that they won't breed in captivity, meaning they can be expensive to continually re-purchase

- Temperature: They'll grow quickly at temperatures of approximately 75-80F (23-26 C). Unfortunately, If the temperature drops below 65F, they will stop eating

- pH: The desired range is 6.5-8.5

Tetra Fish

Some people are surprised to find out that such beautiful fish can be used in an Aquaponic system. They are tiny and are definitely not for eating! They are far more suited to an indoor system due to their size. There is a wide range of different species to choose from, including neon tetras, serape tetras, diamond tetras, cardinal tetras, and glow light tetras, to name but a few. They can make a great feature in your home.

- They grow quickly and are fully grown at around six months

- Tetras cannot compete with other fish species, and they're unlikely to survive

- While I love them, I wouldn't recommend them to beginners unless you have had experience of looking after these fish before, because they are not very hardy and are time-consuming to keep, due to their temperature and pH requirements. Monitoring needs to be done regularly ☺

- Temperature: Approximately 70-81F (21-27C)
- pH: 7-8

Salmon

Salmon are delicious and have a fast growth rate. They aren't always suitable for a home aquaponics system because of their large size. If you have a large outdoor space, however, then Salmon could be a fish worth considering.

Providing you have plenty of space, Salmon are social fish and are extremely friendly and tolerant of each other. They are happy to live in colder temperatures, which make them an ideal fish to keep for those of you in colder climates.

For those of you wanting to eat the fish, salmon are a supremely healthy option. On the flipside, growth can be slower than other fish, and they can take approximately two years to reach full size.

- Salmon can be quite susceptible to diseases, so it is crucial that you source them from a reputable supplier, and monitor the water and your system as a whole on a regular basis

- Temperature: Approximately 55-65F (12-18C)

Acclimatization

Ensure that you have cycled your system first, before purchasing and adding fish. Let the nitrifying bacteria establish themselves. Your fish also need to be given some time to acclimatize, once the time comes to add them to your system. Transferring fish from one tank (or city!) to another can be incredibly stressful for them. Just like us humans, moving gives them a lot to worry about! To acclimatize them properly, you should check the pH of the water they are being transported in, and the pH of the water in your fish tank. If the difference between the two is less than 0.5, then proceed without hesitation. If the difference is more than 0.5, then you will need to give the fish at least 24 hours to adjust. To do this, place your fish into a small aerated tank with their original water and slowly add water from the Aquaponic tank over the course of the day. If the pH difference is less than 0.5, then you only need to get the fish acclimatized to the new temperature. To do this, float the sealed transportation bags in the water of your system's fish tank for around 15 minutes, then add a small amount of water from the tank into the transport water. Leave for 15 minutes to allow the fish to acclimatize. Slowly add a little bit more water, and if all is fine at this point, you are free to add the fish into the new tank! Acclimatization successful.

Stocking Density

It can be difficult to know how many fish you will need in your tank to keep the system running efficiently, without being overstocked. There is no perfect ratio, but a general rule of thumb is 1 lbs of fish (by mass) for every 8 gallons of water. There is some flexibility with this, but I think this rule is a good one to try to stick to. Don't forget to account for fish growth when stocking your tank - 1lb refers to the fully grown weight, not the infantile weight upon introduction to the tank. You can go for a high density, but for a beginner, it is far better to keep it simple, as a higher stocking density requires more equipment and additional aeration to maintain the right amount of oxygen in the tank.

Fish Health

You can typically get a strong indication of how well the entire system is performing by checking the health of the fish, so you must do this daily. You should know the signs of a healthy fish, as well as an unhealthy one. The best time to observe the fish is when you feed them, both before and after you add the food. Healthy fish will have eyes that are shiny and clear, extended fins, and straight tails. They will swim in normal, graceful patterns and will demonstrate a good appetite. Signs of unhealthy fish include lethargy (although it is worth noting Catfish will sleep on the bottom of the tank and feed when they wake up), marks along their body, rubbing or scraping their bodies against the side of the tank, discolored blotches, streaks or lines, and they may shy away from the food, or not eat.

Parasites, fungus, and bacteria can all affect fish. These pathogens can be present in an Aquaponic system from the very beginning, or they can be unfortunately introduced later. This can occur when new fish are put into the tank or when new water is added. Prevention is far better than cure, so it is imperative that you check your water, cycle your system correctly and buy fish only from reputable sources in order to minimize this risk as much as you possibly can. By checking your fish daily, you can hopefully catch any illnesses sooner - and deal with it accordingly, before any more fish fall ill. If only a few fish are affected, then you must remove these immediately, otherwise whatever is affecting them could rapidly spread to the others. If multiple fish are showing signs of illness, then most likely, there is something in the system that is causing distress. Illness could be due to high ammonia levels, incorrect temperature, or high levels of nitrites/nitrates. Carry out water tests, and if anything is unusual, then respond accordingly, and quickly!

Moreover, you should keep an eye on how much food is consumed; only add in a small amount at a time. If you just throw in large amounts, the food that doesn't get eaten will start to decay, using up the oxygen and eventually causing your tank to become an unsafe environment for your fish. If you notice that a lot of fish food hasn't been eaten on one day, then adjust the amount of food you give the fish the next day.

Breeding Fish

If you are planning to raise fish that you can eat, then breeding makes perfect sense. It is a sustainable way of ensuring that you have a constant supply of food, without any additional cost. However, it can also be an Aquaponic hobbyist's nightmare, as some fish don't breed in captivity, while others species are prolific breeders that can end up overloading your tanks.

Assuming that you do want your fish to breed, then the good news is that as long as their living conditions are optimal and they are the type of fish that will happily breed in captivity, then they will pretty much do this on their own without any intervention from you. All you really need to do is keep an eye on your fish. Tell-tale signs to look out for are swimming rapidly, and chasing each other. Some male fish, such as tilapia, become aggressive during breeding, so it is essential to closely monitor your fish if you have species like this - as otherwise, you could end up with absolute carnage in your tank. If you do want your fish to breed, then you should put the fish you want to spawn in a separate container; usually, two males to one female is ideal. The other reason for keeping them separate is that it stops other fish from eating the eggs before they have a chance to hatch.

Whether you are keeping fish purely for the pleasure of doing so, or because you want an organic food source, you should always choose healthy fish to put in your system. It's especially important if you are planning to breed them. High-quality fish will lead to high-quality offspring. If you are deliberately trying to spawn your fish, you will want to choose the best of the best, and pick out the finest specimens from your tank. For most species, a general rule is, the larger the fish - the more offspring will survive.

Harvesting

Many people set up an Aquaponics system with the intention of eating their fish, but then they become pets, and they can't part with them. If you stock your tank with edible fish, then it is entirely up to you whether you eat them or not; just remember if you don't eat them and they breed, you could end up being over-run with fish and need extra tanks. If you have no intention of eating them, you may be better keeping ornamental fish such as Goldfish or tetra. One thing I recommend is that if you do eat your fish, then they will taste a lot better if they have been purged for several days before you harvest them. If you don't happen to know what purging means, it's where you simply remove the fish you want to eat from the main tank - and keep them in a separate fish tank for several days before harvesting them to eat.

Legislation

If you are only buying Goldfish or Koi from your local garden center, or if you are eating all of your produce yourself, then it probably isn't necessary to fill out any forms or register with any sort of governing body.

There is legislation in the UK, specifically, which governs the movement of fish. Therefore, if you wanted to purchase from a fishery or registered farm, or you decided to sell some of your fish or send them back to a fishery, you would need to apply to the Environment Agency for consent. This type of legislation is there to protect fisheries, ensuring any outbreak of disease is appropriately measured and controlled. It may be worth looking into registering with the Fish Health Inspectorate if you live in England or Wales and are setting up an outdoor Aquaponics system: it is a simple form that is quick to fill in, and free. It will allow you to buy fish from a registered farm, which is a bonus because you can be reassured that it will have a biosecurity measures plan (BMP), and therefore the fish you buy are almost guaranteed to be healthy and free from disease or parasites.

If you live in the USA (like me), Canada, or other regions – check the legislation that applies in your country.

Chapter 6 - Plants: Do's & Don'ts

As we have discovered throughout this book, plants aren't *just* a pretty feature of an Aquaponic system - in fact, they are an integral part of the system, and without the plants, aquaponics simply wouldn't be possible. At the time of writing, more than 150 plant species have been grown successfully in home Aquaponic systems, which gives you an awful lot of choice! Most plants do well in this type of system, but some do exceptionally well. As a beginner, I would recommend that you choose those that fall under the latter category. Having said that, if you intend to grow food for yourself or your family, then it doesn't make sense to grow anything that you aren't going to eat. One thing to keep in mind when you are planning your system, is that some plants perform better when using certain aquaponic techniques than when grown with others. For example, if you wanted to grow lettuce, then you would be better placed to use a raft system than a media filled bed system.

You could choose one type of system, set it up, run it successfully for a while and then decide to use a different method and grow different plants. I know growers who started with one small tank and grow bed, growing lettuce and strawberries, that now use a variety (or combination) of systems and have an array of fruit and vegetables, herbs, flowers, and dwarf trees growing in their gardens. Your only limitation is your imagination!

The only plants that I recommend you avoid would be soy, rice, corn, and wheat, as these don't fare well in Aquaponic systems. As a beginner, I would also advise you to steer clear of root vegetables too, as while they are not impossible to grow in Aquaponics, they are definitely more challenging. Start with easy plants, gain experience, and then move on to more difficult ones when you are fully confident in what you are doing. There is nothing more frustrating than setting up an Aquaponic system only to find that nothing grows, or the plants have slower growth than you initially expected. Sometimes, it's not the system itself or your growing skills, but just the type of plants that you've selected!

It is recommended that you begin your journey into Aquaponics with plants that have low nutritional needs, but ones that are also fast-growing and robust. Good 'starter' plants include; lettuce, cucumber, kale, watercress and swiss chard. Once your system is well-established and has been up and running successfully for at least six months, you can consider planting more demanding plants such as tomatoes, cabbage, peppers, strawberries, cauliflower and so on. If you don't want to grow vegetables, you could consider planting pretty flowers such as marigolds or water hyacinths. These can make a visually stunning feature, especially if you stock your tank with ornamental fish alongside them.

Once you detect nitrates in your system, you can start planting. When you first start out, it is wise to use seedlings rather than seeds. The reason for this is because a seed contains everything it needs inside and therefore won't be contributing in any way to your Aquaponics system. In contrast, a seedling will start contributing to the nitrogen cycle immediately. Some people sprinkle seeds in their media bed at the same time, too. In this way, the seeds become embedded and will germinate and fill out the grow bed later, but the seedlings will be there to ensure your system runs correctly from the start. Use seedlings that have been grown in soil, but gently wash the soil off before putting it into your Aquaponics system. Not all growers do this, but I prefer to do so to prevent unnecessary contaminants from being added to my grow beds. A quick dip in a bucketful of water should be enough to wash the soil off. If you wish, you could add seaweed extract or worm juice to this water, in order to provide additional nutrients for the seedlings.

Seedlings can be planted pretty densely in your grow beds, more so than they could in a traditional soil-based garden. This is because they will have access to lots of nutrient-rich water, without competing with other seedlings. Try to maximize your space usage if your system is near a shed, wall, or garden fence - why not build some sort of structure for plants like beans, cucumbers, peas, or tomatoes to climb up? You could also plant 'rambling' vegetables such as pumpkins, in one corner of the grow bed, which can then spill out over the side. It doesn't matter if the side it spreads out to is towards dry and unproductive soil because the pumpkin plant will be receiving all the necessary nutrients it needs from the water tank, and the sections which ramble will be soaking up the sunshine!

The only thing that your plants will need to compete for is sunshine, so plan your space wisely. Consider placing taller plants on the far side of the grow bed so that they don't shade smaller plants (unless you want to do it tactically to grow different plant species with varying requirements of light). Vines such as cucumber and watermelon can be placed on the perimeter and grown outwards.

Stagger your planting regime so that you don't end up harvesting every single crop at the same time. For example, let's say you only planted lettuce in your Aquaponics System, it may make sense to use the whole of your media bed and grow as many lettuces as you possibly can, but of course, they would all be ready at the same time. If you then harvested everything at once, there would be no plants to contribute to and maintain the nitrogen cycle, resulting, as we know, in a high level of nitrates building up in your system. Therefore, it is best if you grow fast-growing plants alongside slower growing ones, or plant seedlings at different times. Whenever you harvest something, always replace it. This is where sprinkling seeds into an established system can help; by the time the seedlings have started to mature, your seeds will have germinated and will be contributing to the system and the nitrogen cycle. Another advantage of staggering your growing and harvesting is that you will always have a continual supply of fresh vegetables. You should always have plants growing in at least half of your grow bed. When fast-growing plants are harvested, replace them with slow-growing ones, and vice versa. This may sound strange, but the plants that are the most beneficial to your system are the ones in the initial growth stages, due to their increased nitrate uptake.

While an Aquaponics system can, to some extent, extend planting seasons, it is recommended that you still follow seasonal planting guidelines to give your plants the best possible environmental conditions. Those which aren't native to you, or are planted out of season, won't always thrive and therefore won't be so beneficial to your aquaponic garden.

Some crops grow better in warmer climates. Crops that do better in a warm environment include garlic, parsnip, shallots, artichoke, chives, and parsley. Crops that grow well in colder climates include cabbage, cauliflower, herbs, brussels sprouts, horseradish, carrots, potatoes, sweet potatoes, onions, squash, and beets.

You may need to stake some of your plants if they are top-heavy and likely to blow over easily, or also if you live in a climate where winds are often powerful. If you do use stakes, it is key that they are not treated wooden ones and that they are not pushed too deep inside the grow media.

One thing many people extensively worry about when they first start an Aquaponics system, is that their seedlings aren't instantly flourishing. There can be deficiencies in plant health, which leads to slow growth. Don't panic; this is perfectly normal and happens because the nutrient supply is low while the microbe colony is being established. For this reason, for the first 3 months, plants in an Aquaponic system tend to exhibit a slower growth rate compared to later down the line, when it's in full swing. If your system is running correctly, then within one or two months, your leafy green vegetables should be ready to harvest. As mentioned previously, I always recommend planting leafy greens because they are great for beginners and are fast-growing. After your system has been running for three months or more, you should have bigger microbial colonies to support larger fruiting plants, such as tomatoes.

Plants that are in their early stages of growth need a lot of iron, but a new Aquaponics System tends to lack this - thus, you may need to supplement using soluble iron in a powdered form (chelated iron) until your system is fully established. The recommendation is 1-2mg of iron per liter of water in the first three months, after which, adding it whenever iron deficiencies are detected will be sufficient. Seaweed extract is another good supplement to use, as it usually has very high levels of most micronutrients and minerals. It is sold under various brand names around the world and can be either a liquid or a powder. Sometimes, seaweed extract is extracted by boiling, but, if you have a choice, a liquid that has been extracted via crushing is far better as it will also contain humic acid. Whatever you use, just ensure it is 'Aquaponics safe.' If you use a high-quality aquaculture feed, then you shouldn't have an issue with plant deficiencies once the system has established.

The feed rate ratio is the main guideline to balance the amount of fish feed to plant growing area. For leafy greens, the feed rate ratio is 20-

50g per meter squared daily, whereas, for fruiting vegetables, it is 50-80g per meter squared daily.

While you shouldn't get deficiencies in your plants once the system is up and running, occasionally, you might find that your plants are lacking some essential nutrients, especially when you are first venturing into Aquaponics. Often the type of fish you are keeping, and the food you use will dictate which nutrients are missing.

Plants deficient in nutrients won't be healthy, won't thrive, and therefore won't be as tasty because plants need a varied diet just like we humans do. Stunted growth, low or nil production, yellowing or off-colored leaves, and even parts dying off, are all visible signs of a nutrient deficiency in a plant. When we talk about nutrients, we are referring to the elements that the plants can absorb through the water. The most important ones in your Aquaponics system are potassium, nitrogen, phosphorous, magnesium, calcium, and sulfur. Your plants will also need copper, zinc, chloride, iron, boron, manganese, and molybdenum - but only in trace amounts.

There exists both mobile and immobile nutrients. Mobile nutrients are ones that move through your plant. Any deficiencies will be noticeable in the older leaves first, because the available nutrients will move primarily to the newer leaves. Examples of mobile nutrients include phosphorous, potassium, chloride, nitrogen, magnesium, and molybdenum. For immobile nutrients, a deficiency will be initially noticeable in the newer leaves, because the nutrient would still be present in the older leaves. Immobile nutrients include calcium, iron, zinc, sulfur, manganese, boron, and copper.

The most common deficiencies to watch out for are **iron**, **calcium**, **potassium**, and **phosphorus**. Let's look at each in turn:

If your plants have yellowish growth, then this is usually indicative of an **iron** deficiency. Iron is one of the very few nutrients that isn't supplied adequately via fish food. As mentioned above, you can use Chelated Iron. The guidelines on Chelated Iron is 1-2mg/liter, and should be added every 3-4 weeks as and when it's needed.

The tell-tale sign of **calcium** deficiency is localized tissue necrosis. The easiest way to treat a calcium deficiency is using a spray made up of Calcium Chloride mixed with water. For every gallon of water, use 4 teaspoons of Calcium Chloride. However, I would always start with less and increase if needed. Spray once a week.

When there is a **phosphorous** deficiency, the only indication is usually stunting during early growth stages. Phosphorous is essential to healthy plant growth. Rock phosphate is an excellent source of phosphorous - you should be able to purchase this in your local garden center. It can be added directly to your plant beds, allowing the roots to absorb it almost immediately. A word of caution - if your grow bed is in direct sunlight, it may dissolve before the plant can absorb it. If you can get hold of shellfish bones, you can add these to your fish tank to increase both the calcium and phosphorous levels.

Brown scorching or yellowing between leaf veins are hints to a lack of **potassium.** Potassium is often difficult to supply to your plants, because if you add it as a supplement - it can react with the calcium and magnesium present in the system, *reducing* it before your plants can use it. To ensure your potassium is absorbed effectively, make sure you monitor the calcium and magnesium levels, and keep them balanced. To increase potassium, you can use potassium chloride and spray the plants directly once a week, or use kelp meal concentrate, another good source of potassium. You could alternatively add potassium sulfate or potassium hydroxide.

Often, plants show signs of what appears to be a nutrient deficiency, when in fact, they could be suffering from transport stress or disease. Equally, the water quality could be poor, or pH levels could be whacked out. If your plants are struggling, rather than assuming it's a nutrient deficiency - and dosing them with all manner of supplements, check your full system first, measuring all the different variables we talked about previously. To make matters more complicated, plants can be deficient in more than one thing, or you could have a pest problem, as well as a nutrient problem. Often, it is like playing detective, monitor everything, and then rule out different things one by one.

It is imperative to try and prevent pests from entering your system. Tactics could include the use of physical barriers, companion plants, crop rotation, trapping, and so on. Only if pests are a persisting problem that aren't going away should you consider using sprays. Always ensure that you only use sprays which are Aquaponic safe.

Some sprays made of plant extracts, essential oil extracts, soft soaps, or plant oils may be safe to use in an Aquaponics System but, if used, should never be sprayed directly into the water, just to be air on the side of caution. For sap-sucking insects, many people have found success with chili and garlic sprays, but even when using organic sprays, excessive use is never recommended.

- Bacillus Thuringiensis is a soil-dwelling bacterium that is used as a pesticide against creatures such as caterpillars and can be found online under a variety of different brand names. Ensure that the spray is organically certified and safe for Aquaponics.

- If you have a slug problem, you could fill a small saucer with beer; the slugs will be attracted to it - but then will drown, allowing you to dispose of them effectively.

- Aphids, Whiteflies, and Thrips can be caught by using colored sticky traps. Then, you have the added advantage of being able to count how many of these infest your Aquaponics System.

- If you find a lot of mold and fungus on your plants, a potassium bicarbonate spray is often effective. Again, this is sold under various brand names around the world. Your system will also appreciate the added potassium, and the bicarbonate can be helpful in raising the pH.

You can remove pests manually, either by hand or by gently sweeping them away with a paintbrush. The downside is that this is time-consuming, and insects are great at camouflaging themselves, and can be so tiny that it's difficult to spot them. You definitely need a lot of time and patience to do this every day.

In the wild, pests are kept at bay by natural elements such as temperature, rain, and wind. Rain prevents winged insects from flying, and droplets can knock them off plants. You can recreate these weather phenomena by using a spray bottle filled with the aquarium water (not tap water, because remember this can contain chlorine and other damaging chemicals) to replicate the rain. Wind can be mimicked by using a fan, and temperature can be controlled with the use of heaters.

One natural way of keeping pests at bay is to use companion planting - by growing either sacrificial plants to attract pests to them (and away from the ones you want to eat) or by planting symbiotic plants that will deter insects by taste or scent.

So which insects might be present and why are they bad news?

Aphids (also known as greenfly/whitefly) are minute, little creatures that are almost colorless or else green, black, or possibly brown. These insects feed on the sap of the plants, either by taking it from the phloem vessels or by sucking the xylem sap. When their food sources are in short supply, they produce offspring with wings to go and search for new food.

Aphids have a symbiotic relationship with ants, in that the ants will defend aphids from attack. Sometimes they will store aphid eggs in their nests over winter and carry them out to a plant when they hatch. The aphids, in return, let the ants 'milk' them for honeydew by stroking the aphids' bodies with their antennae. This honeydew can cause mold to grow on the plants, so if you see aphids, you may also discover that you have an ant infestation as well as an aphid one.

An aphid infestation can be detrimental to your system, as aphids can quickly destroy plants. Any plants that are found to be infested should be removed from the system immediately so that the aphids don't reach the healthy plants. If you do remove any crops, take care not to scatter any aphids onto other plants. Once the infected plant is removed from your system, you should manually remove the aphids. If the infestation continues after this, there are some biological ways to control them.

Firstly you can use ladybirds; they eat aphids and mites and other soft-scale insects. Their life span is approximately one year, and in this time, can each consume thousands of aphids, with their larvae eating around four hundred aphids before they reach the pupal stage.

Wasps are not many people's favorite insect, but with this unique method of biological control, you can use wasps to your advantage. The approach involves introducing tiny specialist wasps which lay their eggs, later eating the aphids as they hatch. It was a widely used method for aphid control in greenhouses in the 1920s, but was eventually replaced with chemical pesticides. More and more people are shying away from chemical methods nowadays, especially when using alternative gardening techniques, such as Aquaponics.

Another problematic pest is the **spider mite**. Technically classified as arachnids rather than insects, these creatures feed on a variety of plants. Adult spider mites tend to be reddish-brown in color and oval-shaped. If you have an infestation, you may notice silk webbing (similar to spider webs) before you see the spider mites themselves, due to their minuscule size. They breed when it is hot and dry, with females laying up to twenty eggs a day. To reduce the risk of a spider mite infestation, you should ensure your system is well ventilated. If you do notice spider mites on your plants, you can introduce predatory mites that reproduce at twice the rate of spider mites when the temperature is above 65F. The predatory mites will consume up to five adult spider mites, or twenty of their eggs per day. Another option is to introduce ladybirds, which also eat spider mites.

Not everybody will be fond of the idea of introducing other insects to their plants, and I can understand this. Some people worry they are just replacing one pest with another, while others are just squeamish about all creepy-crawlies! Luckily, there are some organic pesticides or antifeedants that can be used in an Aquaponics system safely. For clarification, when I talk about pesticides, I am referring to sprays that kill the pests, whereas antifeedants are sprays that repel the pests to discourage them from settling on the plants.

Absolutely no harsh or synthetic chemicals can be used in your Aquaponics system because they can destroy your bacterial colony, as well as your aquaculture. Everything needs to be organic, so please ensure you check before you use anything harmful to your plants. If you are not sure, then please don't use it. Another important point is to *remove* the plants *before* you treat them. This not only prevents other plants from becoming infested but also ensures nothing gets into the water that could be harmful to the fish. For example, if you use a soap-based spray, it can stun the fish. Chilli or garlic sprays can harm their eyes.

The following are listed as 'safe' because they are considered organic. Neem Seed Oil inhibits pests feeding, reduces their mobility, prevents them from molting, and disrupts their eggs, pupae, and larvae. It should only be used sparingly. Non-toxic mineral oils have the added benefit of controlling any mildew or fungal problems you may also encounter. These tend to be synthesized from fatty acids such as vegetable or coconut oil or natural soap. They are easy to make at home and are effective at killing aphids and mites.

If you plant chili, chive, onions, garlic, or mustard in your Aquaponic system between other plants, they can successfully repel both pests and fungus. If you do still find you have an infestation, you can use the fruit from these plants, mixed with washing up liquid and diluted with water to make a spray.

Remember, pests aren't limited to just insects and bugs; you may have to battle against larger pests, for example, rabbits, squirrels, badgers, mice, rats, birds, and so on. Fences will usually suffice as protection here.

Whatever technique you are using (NFT, DWC, Media Filled Beds), whenever you are harvesting your plants, you need to make sure the whole root system is removed. If you are using a media such as gravel, then a quick shake should be sufficient enough to remove any entangled in the roots. Gravel can be returned to the media bed. Any discarded roots can be placed into a compost bin if you have one. It is not advised that you leave any roots or leaves in the Aquaponics system because it can encourage disease. Use a sharp, clean pair of scissors, or a knife. Once harvested, place the plants in a clean bag ready to wash and chill as soon as possible, to keep them fresh.

Any good gardener will tell you a garden is continually changing and is an ongoing project. Aquaponics is no different. Sometimes, you will plant crops that thrive and grow incredibly well. Other times you won't! Don't be afraid to experiment. It is incredibly satisfying to see your plants grow and thrive, and it's equally rewarding to harvest and *taste the fruits of your labor.*

Chapter 7 - Daily, Weekly & Monthly Maintenance Best Practises

Once your system is up and running, there are some day to day activities that you'll need to be doing in order to maintain it. Some of these tasks will be daily, others are weekly, and the remainder can just be done once a month. We'll look at each of these in turn now!

Daily

The daily maintenance is actually relatively simple, but it's imperative – so please don't neglect it!

- You will need to feed your fish. When you first set up your system, the fish you use will most likely not be fully grown, and therefore they'll need feeding 2-3 times a day. This can be reduced to once or twice a day once they mature. You can buy automatic fish feeders, and there is nothing wrong with using these feeders, but sometimes - if you have a large amount of fish, feeders can't always keep up with the demands required. Personally, I prefer hand feeding because you can check the health of your fish at the same time, and can see how much feed is getting eaten .vs. how much goes to waste.

- You should check each fishes' behavior and appearance, so that you can act quickly if something is wrong. Sadly, sometimes fish die, so they will need removing from the tank.

- Check the water and air pumps to ensure they are working well. Look for any blockages, clear these if evident, and then check that water is flowing freely throughout the system.

- Depending upon the climate in which you live and the interior temperature of your tanks, water may evaporate, and you could end up losing up to 10% of your water volume. Low water levels can affect your fish, so monitor this daily and add extra water as and when necessary.

- If the water temperature drops by too much, your fish can become lethargic and stop eating - eventually, they could die. Therefore, it is important to check this daily. I would recommend that you check and make a note of the difference between daytime and night temperature (when it suits your schedule) if your system is located outdoors.

- You should monitor the ammonia, nitrite, nitrate, DO, and pH levels using your test kits daily. As well as writing these levels down, you should make adjustments where necessary. I have put this on the 'things to do daily' list, because this book is aimed at beginners, and I recommend that when you set up your first Aquaponics system, you monitor everything more carefully. Once your system is up and running successfully, and you are happy with what you are doing - you can track these levels every week if you find it easier.

• Check your entire Aquaponic system for any leaks, sometimes these could go unnoticed, so it is important you actively check.

• Remove any solids from the clarifier and rinse any filters.

• Check the plants and remove pests if present. Remove any sick or dead plants and branches.

Weekly

• Clear any fish waste from the biofilter and from the bottom of the fish tank.

• Check the plant roots and ensure that they are not blocking the flow of water, or any pipes.

• Check the plants for any deficiencies and act accordingly.

• Fish harvesting is a challenging one to classify into a daily, weekly, or monthly list, because once your fish are large enough to eat - then it is entirely up to you when you harvest them, and it will be dependent upon how many you want to eat.

Seeding, rotating, and harvesting plants will be a monthly or less frequent than a monthly task, depending on what you plant and when you plant it.

Monthly

Our monthly tasks include:

- Stocking new fish into the tanks; of course, this is only if necessary if your fish haven't been breeding, and if you've been removing some.
- Clean the clarifier, biofilter, and all other filters.
- Clean the bottom of the fish tank using nets.

COMMON BEGINNER MISTAKES IN AQUAPONICS

One of the first mistakes that people make is not cycling their system properly initially; they add their fish and plants too soon, out of excitement. A lack of cycling creates a less than perfect environment for the new fish and plants to thrive. There may be high levels of ammonia in your system if you haven't allowed time for the beneficial bacteria to start colonising. Ammonia could build up to levels that are toxic, leading to devastating results. Always wait at least 3-6 weeks in order to give your system the time to fully cycle - unless you inoculate, in which case, you can get started sooner!

A second mistake is introducing unhealthy fish into the system. Sadly, not all fish are raised clean and disease-free. Those found in the wild can carry disease – not all of them, but enough to pose a significant risk to your system. Make sure you get off to a good start by only using fish that have been certified as clean and disease-free.

Poor water quality is another common issue newcomers face; they cycle their systems properly, but don't test their water regularly enough. As you'll now know, there are 5 key parameters; pH, Dissolved Oxygen (DO), Temperature, Cleanliness, and Purity. Some people forget to test tap water for chlorine and fluoride; remember, if the tap/mains water contains high levels of chlorine, then let it stand in a container for 48 hours to dissipate. My second piece of advice is to buy a water testing kit and use it regularly, from the moment you start to add water to your system.

If your plants have taken on a yellowish tinge, you might immediately assume that there is an iron deficiency. While this may be true, it could also be that your pH is too high. If pH rises too far above 7.0, plants will struggle to absorb iron effectively, no matter how much is present in the growing medium. This is why it is vital to continually monitor the pH of the system.

Growers who are brand new to Aquaponics can get extremely excited, and they put far too many fish into the tank, without considering the water to fish ratio. Their fish tanks become overcrowded, resulting in high nitrate levels. This can lead to stunted growth and even death! I recommended that you keep your stocking density lower when you are first starting. It is far safer this way. The recommended density is one pound of fish for every 8 gallons of water. When you are calculating your fish to water ratio, remember to account for the fully grown fish, not the baby fish that you start out with.

If your plant leaves start to take on a deep green or black hue, then this is a sign that your plants are absorbing too much nitrogen. This can be due to having too many fish excreting so much ammonia, that can't be converted to nitrites/nitrates fast enough by the bacteria. One solution is to plant some more seedlings/seeds, assuming you some spare room. Alternatively, remove some fish from your system.

Are you feeding your fish? This sounds silly, I know, but trust me, I've seen it time and time again. Fish can survive a long time without being fed, *but* this isn't helpful for your plants, which rely on excretions of the fish to be converted into nutrients that they can absorb. If you can't manually feed your fish consistently, preferably twice a day, then invest in an automatic feeder to do the job for you – or ask a family member.

The flipside to underfeeding is overfeeding. Only provide enough so that the fish are consuming the food for only a couple of minutes. If you put in too much, and it is left uneaten, it can start to decay inside the tank. If any food is left uneaten, remove it after half an hour, and give less the following day.

Growing the wrong plants is another issue. To ensure that your plants do well, refer back to Chapter 6 to see which species of plants suit your situation best. Match up your fish and plants correctly; for example, if you are keeping ornamental tropical fish, guess what? They like warm water, but not all plants will!

Check that your plants are getting enough light. People come to me time and time again, saying that their fish are doing fine, their water parameters are near enough perfect, and yet their plants aren't growing. Often the problem is that their system is indoors, or hidden in the shade for most of the day. Plants grow via photosynthesis. If you have no access to real sunlight, use LED grow lights on a timer. They're cheap and work just fine. Another mistake that newbies make is selecting an incorrectly sized water pump. Consider the water volume and height between the plants and the fish tank.

Most of us have jobs, families, households to run, and so many commitments that sometimes we feel like we have no time. I find people say, "I forgot to check my Aquaponics system today. I'll do it tomorrow." Tomorrow comes, and they forget again, or they go out, throw a bit of food to the fish, do a brief once over of the plants, and think "everything looks healthy, I'll monitor properly tomorrow." The cycle persists, forming weak monitoring habits. While an Aquaponics system is pretty low maintenance, you do need to carry out water testing, as well as fish and plant checks. It only takes a day or two for one slight change that's gone unnoticed, to jeopardize your whole system. This is one scenario where prevention really is far superior to cure!

Chapter 8 - Nitrifying Bacteria And Vermiponics

Nitrifying Bacteria

Science time! Let's chat about the beneficial bacteria. Without it, the plants wouldn't be able to filter the water as efficiently, nor would they have as high an intake of nutrients. Moreover, the fish waste wouldn't be broken down and would eventually build up until the system became toxic. Bacteria therefore, forms the vital link between the plants and the fish, allowing them to live harmoniously together.

There are three main groups of bacteria which are needed, if an Aquaponics system is going to function as it should.

The first group are **Ammonia-oxidizing bacteria**, which convert ammonia (which is toxic to fish) into nitrites. Next are **Nitrite-oxidizing**

bacteria, which then convert these nitrites into nitrates - which are the most available form of nutrients for the plants. Finally, there are also **Heterotrophic bacteria** that break down the solid waste from plants and fish, into micro-nutrients also needed for plant growth.

Collectively, the ammonia and nitrite-oxidizing bacteria are referred to as nitrifying bacteria. To encourage good bacteria to develop, you need to ensure the environmental factors are correct. pH levels should be between 6.0-7.5, with a water temperature of around 60-85F. Bacteria can survive at a broader range of temperatures than this, but they may struggle to reproduce, and productivity would decline. In colder months, you should monitor your ammonia levels extra closely, even if your system has been running perfectly fine for months. One issue that Aquaponic growers have come across is that once the bacteria have been established and the owners have become a bit complacent with their monitoring, and then the cold months hit. The bacterial colonies within the system stop working, leading to the water becoming toxic without the owner even realizing!

Luckily, nitrifying bacteria enjoy an oxygen-rich environment, as do your plants and fish. Another good reason for keeping your system well-oxygenated is that it deters most of the other types of bacteria that are harmful to your system, such as sulfate-reducing bacteria and denitrifying bacteria.

The beneficial bacteria need to be protected from the sun's harmful rays, as they are photosensitive. Sunlight also encourages algae to grow, which can clog up system components and prevent the effectiveness of the bacteria. Although the media in your grow beds will provide some protection for the bacteria, you should locate your system in a shaded area if possible, depending on the plants you're growing.

Some growers become so impatient and add their fish before the bacteria have had time to colonize adequately. This results in poor fish health or even death because the ammonia and nitrite levels are just too high. It is not easy to physically measure the population of the bacteria. However, a brownish slime in the biofilter, or on other surfaces in the system, is a sure sign that you have a thriving colony. What you can measure however, is the level of nitrites, nitrates, and ammonia. Unless you have nitrifying bacteria in your system, you won't get a nitrite or nitrate reading. You should aim for ammonia and nitrite levels below 1mg per liter, and as close to zero as possible. Once you have cycled your system and have this reading, you are ready to add plants and fish to your system.

Nitrifying bacteria can be sourced from Aquaponic/Aquaculture stores or websites - as a liquid. Alternatively, you can use 'live water' or biofilter media from an established Aquaponics system. If you take it from the latter, make sure the system is disease-free. However, unless you know somebody who has their own Aquaponics system, this isn't going to be easy to source. Adding nitrifying bacteria to your system immediately isn't a replacement for the cycling process because your bacteria still need time to colonize until it reaches a level that can support the fish. It just makes cycling that little bit quicker.

Worms & Vermiponics

Vermiponics is a means of growing plants without soil. Instead of nutrients being provided by fish waste, the nutrient solution in vermiponics is made from worm-tea (worm castings). Instead of looking at vermiponics alone (i.e., growing plants without using fish), this chapter looks at how we can combine vermiponics with Aquaponics to provide the best possible environment when using a media-filled bed system.

Microbes in the gut of the worm help to mineralize and oxidize organic matter consumed by the worm to produce vermicast or worm-castings, also referred to as 'worm manure' or 'worm humus.' These worm-castings contain water-soluble nutrients such as nitrogen, phosphates, calcium, magnesium, and potash, which are all highly beneficial for plants. If you have a wormery already, you could also use the liquid at the bottom of this – also known as 'worm tea.' It is entirely up to you whether you set up your own wormery or put the worms straight into an Aquaponics grow bed.

You don't *have* to add worms to your Aquaponics System, and you would be able to grow plants perfectly well without them, but there are numerous benefits to having worms in your media beds. Firstly, worms break down solid waste, whether this is fish excrement that hasn't been broken down, uneaten fish food or material from the plants such as dead leaves and roots. There are two benefits to this; firstly, the microbes inside the worms break this down further, and the excrement from the worms then feeds the plants. Moreover, you don't need to filter out the solid waste or clean out your media beds as often as you would if the worms weren't present.

Secondly, studies have shown that worm-castings and 'worm tea' can protect plants from diseases and parasites, as well as insects such as aphids, spider mites, tomato hornworms, and mealy bugs. Not only that, but because of the additional nutrients the worms provide, you can finish up with larger plants and a higher yield.

< https://news.cornell.edu/stories/2011/12/research-worm-compost-can-suppress-plant-disease >

Another added benefit is that if you become overrun with worms, you can feed them to your fish, as they provide protein and are a great supplement to their diet.

One concern many people have when I discuss adding worms into their Aquaponics system (aside from some being a bit squeamish) is that of the worms drowning. They often point out the fact that when rain falls, worms crawl out of their lovely underground homes and congregate on the sidewalk where they either dry up in the sun or are easy prey for birds. This is because worms cannot survive in waterlogged soil; they would drown. In actual fact, it isn't the water that bothers the worms. It's that the water forces oxygen out of the soil, so the worms have to come out for air. What does an Aquaponics system have lots of, other than water? Oxygen! The aerated water in your system will be highly oxygenated, not only that but the flood and drain action (if that's the method you are using) pulls oxygen into the grow bed media. As a result, worms thrive in this environment. More so, some people have reported finding worms happily living in their sump tank as well as their media beds! A lot of folks also worry about worms reproducing until they are overrun with them, but actually, these creatures adjust to their conditions; once they start to become overpopulated, their reproduction will slow down or even stop altogether. So don't worry about that one.

So how should you introduce worms into your system? Like anything else, you need to do so with extreme caution. I'm not recommending you go outside, dig up a few earthworms and add them right into your media beds. This would do more harm than good, and you could end up introducing disease into your system. I should also point out here, that when I talk about adding worms to your system, I'm not actually referring to those you commonly find in your garden. The best ones to add are red composting worms because these are the type that love feeding on decaying / dead plant debris, and are always looking for food. Of course, you will need to get these worms shipped to you and, just as you would when purchasing fish, always choose a supplier that is trustworthy and professional, preferably with great reviews if you are selecting them from the internet. Any vermiculturalist worth their salt won't ship worms in manure or compost because the heat given off is detrimental to the worms. A trustworthy source should wash their worms at least twice after removing them from their home and should ship in peat moss or similar; it is worth checking how they are shipped before purchasing to ensure that the supplier knows what they are talking about. If you are worried, you can purge the worms before adding them into their system by putting them in wet cornmeal, cream of wheat or oatmeal for twenty-four hours, washing them thoroughly, and then putting them into the system by laying them on top of the grow beds. They will soon crawl into your media due to their dislike of bright light.

One thing you should beware of is that some people have said that they have caught their worms having a feast on their onions, carrots, or other root vegetables. The only time I have ever noticed this personally, however, is when the vegetables had already started to rot, and the worms were eating the decaying matter. As long as there is enough fish waste and decaying plant material for them to eat, they shouldn't start munching their way through your precious crops.

My recommendation is that once you have released the worms into your grow bed, just leave them - resist the temptation to keep searching for them. There is plenty of oxygen and food for them to thrive, and you won't necessarily see them because they are good at hiding. The only time you should see them is when you find them entwined with the roots - when you pull out a plant. Take care to look for them at that point, so you can carefully add them back into the media bed.

Conclusion

Aquaponics is a powerful combination of Aquaculture and Hydroponics; it's a unique way of growing plants in water while simultaneously raising fish. Taking advantage of the Nitrogen cycle, an Aquaponics system works when nitrifying bacteria breaks down fish waste into nutrients. A water pump then carries the nutrient-rich water up to the grow beds, where the plants use the nutrients, effectively cleaning the water, which is then carried back down to the fish tank. The fish, plants, and nitrifying bacteria have a harmonious, symbiotic relationship, each one reliant on the next for the system to work successfully.

There are numerous advantages over both soil-based gardening techniques and Hydroponic ones - including sustainability, the ability to adapt systems to your own needs, and the ability to grow food anywhere from large gardens to small apartments. Not only that, but plants in Aquaponic systems tend to produce higher yields, with faster growth rates, as linked studies have demonstrated.

There is a long list of components needed for one of these unique systems, with the most important elements being the fish, plants, the bacteria, and the grow bed. There's a whole array of secondary components, like fish food, water testing kits, and so on, and so on. The list can seem endless, but once the system is set up, there is very little you need to purchase on a recurring basis.

The water is the lifeblood of the system, and it is therefore incredibly important that you test it regularly, preferably on a daily basis when you are setting up a new system. This can be dropped down to twice a week, or weekly, once you are confident that your system is running successfully. Issues can quickly escalate if you aren't careful, so it is recommended that not only do you test your water, but you also record each reading every time. The five water quality parameters you will need to test for are; pH, Dissolved Oxygen (DO), Temperature, Cleanliness, and Purity.

Before you use any water in your system, you must test it and treat it - removing any chemicals such as Chlorine or Chloramine that would harm the wellbeing of your fish. Water testing kits are fairly easy to use, usually exploiting color changes to indicate results. Maintaining the correct levels for each water parameter is a delicate balancing act. The key to success is finding a happy medium for each one, so it is advisable to plan your system carefully, matching up fish and plants based on water quality parameters that they can both share.

The physical building of a system can put many people off, but it far outweighs the eye-wateringly alternative of buying a pre-made one. As well as the satisfaction you will gain, having made something with your own two hands; you will also understand it far better and therefore be able to solve any issues that may arise since you'll know every single component that is used within it. Not only that, but building your own system allows you to customize it to suit your growing and spatial needs.

When it comes to selecting the type of system to use, there are a variety to choose from. I personally recommend that a beginner starts with the Media Filled Beds technique because it is easier to set up, less can go wrong, and there is a large surface area for nitrifying bacteria to colonize. There are also a variety of plants you can grow with this technique, and once you have mastered the simple ones, you can move onto move challenging ones should you wish to do so.

The grow bed media also acts as a filter for any solid waste, and if you wished, you could add red worms to this to break down this waste even further. You can use a variety of containers for the grow bed itself. On the contrary, bear in mind that the container needs to be strong and hard-wearing, as it will not only be holding your plants, but the grow bed media and water too. The media is something else you must consider carefully, and while you have a multitude of options to choose from - it needs to be limestone-free, else it will affect the pH of your water. It should also not be overly fine, as this will trap water.

Deep Water Culture (DWC) - also known as a Raft or Floating system - is another option, although it isn't so highly recommended for beginners, because not only can it be more complex to set up and operate, it doesn't enable such a wide variety of plants to be grown like the Media Filled Beds technique. With this type of system, plants are grown on polystyrene foam raft boards that float on top of the water. The plant roots then hang directly into the water, rather than being buried in media. Beneficial bacteria will grow throughout the system, although it can be harder to cultivate unless your tank is highly aerated. If you are trying this technique as a beginner, I would stick to growing leafy greens such as lettuce, because they tend to thrive and are harder to get wrong!

Another method you might opt for is the Nutrient Film Technique (NFT). This is actually a Hydroponic technique that has been adapted for Aquaponics. Plants are grown in long, thin channels where water flows continuously, providing roots with nutrient-rich water. Once the water reaches the end of the channel, it returns to the sump tank (if one is connected to the system) or the fish tank.

Keep in mind that whatever system you choose, all components are required to be food-grade quality material and should be free from harsh chemicals. If you are using anything that is recycled/upcycled from something else, make sure you wash it thoroughly before utilizing it in your Aquaponics system, because otherwise, you could set yourself up for failure, contaminating your water before you even start.

Each method has its advantages and disadvantages, and which one you choose will be dependent upon your personal preference and which one excites you the most. Some prefer media filled beds because they are used to soil gardening and having something to 'dig' into, or because they are interested in using worms. Others will prefer the raft system because they think it looks better or because they don't like the idea of having to touch and handle grow media all of the time.

Location, climate, or the amount of space you have available could also influence your decision over which aquaponic technique you want to use. Access to shielded electrical outlets is also necessary, remember.

Aquaponic Systems can be set up in five super easy steps;

Firstly, source your fish tank. When it comes to choosing your fish tank, it is no different to regular fish keeping in that you still need a good amount of space for your fish to swim freely, and you'll still need a pump to keep your tank aerated. The only difference is that this tank will be connected to a grow bed. The pump and pipes will send water up to the grow beds, and back to the tank. It is wise to have your fish tank on a stand if you are using a normal rectangular aquarium style, because that way, you have space for all of the plumbing underneath and the tank will be well supported. Select your tank based on which fish you'll keep, not forgetting that some species prefer dark environments, while other, ornamental fish might prefer a transparent glass tank.

The next step is to build your grow bed, either above or to the side of the fish tank. If you are limited in space, the grow bed generally goes above the fish tank. Build the grow bed on a stand to help withstand all the weight it will need to hold. If you are doing the media filled bed option, then simply fill it with your chosen media, whether this be clay pebbles, gravel, etc. Whichever media you use needs to be pH-neutral and should hold moisture well, so your plants don't dry out.

Once built, add water and cycle your system. Finally, add the fish, then the plants. The type of fish you raise may also be dependent on whether you are planning to eat your fish, or not. Do you want to make your aquaponic system into an ornamental feature, that is a talking point for anyone who enters your home? If so, you may be best poised to choose tropical fish, such as Neon Tetra. On the other hand, if your aquaponic system is being set up so that you can be as sustainable as possible, growing both plants and fish for food, you might raise Trout, or Tilapia in an outdoor tank, for example. As silly as it sounds, the decision about whether your fish will be considered food or pets is one that you need to think carefully before you set up your system. All that is left to do then, is to maintain the system - which is usually pretty simple if you feed your fish a high-quality diet and test the water regularly. One word of warning is not to go too big at the beginning; start small and work your way up; it is far better (and less disheartening) if you inadvertently kill ten or fifteen fish than if you kill five-hundred!

So there you have it: whichever Aquaponic system you use, this is going to be an incredibly fun adventure for you - don't be afraid to experiment and when you do face problems, see them as learning opportunities and as a way to improve your skills. Most of all, your system should be a hobby, not a chore, so relax and have some fun!

I really hope that you've enjoyed reading my book, and best of luck on your new aquaponic journey!

Margaret Fisher

If you've enjoyed reading this book and enjoyed learning everything there is to know about all aspects of aquaponics, please consider leaving a 5* review on Amazon. It will mean a lot to me to see that you have enjoyed reading this book as much I've enjoyed writing it!

References

Woods, Robert. (2019, February 19). How To Grow With Aquaponics In 5 Simple Steps. Retrieved March 20, 2020,

From https://learn.eartheasy.com/articles/how-to-grow-with-aquaponics-in-5-simple-steps/

Castelo, J. (2018, July 05). What Is Aquaponics: A Very Fertile Beginners Guide. Retrieved March 20, 2020.

From https://worldwaterreserve.com/aquaponics/what-is-aquaponics/

CANNA UK (2019, January, 18) Growing With Aquaponics. Retrieved March 20, 2020.

From http://www.canna-uk.com/aquaponics

Calderone, L. (2018, December 26). Growing With Hydroponics, Aeroponics and Aquaponics. Retrieved March 20, 2020.

From https://www.agritechtomorrow.com/article/2018/05/growing-with-hydroponics-aeroponics-and-aquaponics/10733

Radin, S. (2016, December 02). Aquaponic Systems For Beginners. Retrieved March 20, 2020.

http://www.aquaponicsbuzz.com/aquaponic-systems-for-beginners/

Brooke, N. (2020, February 25). The Best Plants for Aquaponics. Retrieved March 20, 2020.

From https://www.howtoaquaponic.com/plants/best-plants-for-aquaponics/

Green And Vibrant.com (2019, August 08). 15 DIY Aquaponic Plans You Can Actually Build. Retrieved March 20, 2020.

From
https://www.greenandvibrant.com/aquaponic-plans

Sallenave, R. (2016, October) Important Water Quality Parameters In Aquaponics Systems. Retrieved March 20, 2020.

From
https://aces.nmsu.edu/pubs/_circulars/CR680.pdf

Aquaponics Exposed (2017, February 06) Aquaponic System Components. Retrieved March 20, 2020.

From
https://aquaponicsexposed.com/aquaponic-system-components/

Goering, C. (2019, May 01). Types of Aquaponics Designs. Retrieved March 20, 2020.

From
https://www.ecolifeconservation.org/updates/types-aquaponics-systems-design/

Oregon Aquaponics (2014, January 15) Backyard Aquaponics Project. Retrieved March 20, 2020.

From https://oregonaquaponics.wordpress.com/types-of-systems/

Lets Tend The Garden (2019, November 12) Comprehensive Guide On How To Build An Aquaponics System. Retrieved March 20, 2020.

From https://www.letstendthegarden.org/how-to-build-an-aquaponics-system/

Aquaponics Alive (2013, April 24). Pros And Cons Of Different System Types. Retrieved March 20, 2020.

From https://aquaponicsalive.blogspot.com/2013/04/pros-and-cons-of-different-system-types.html

Vergeer, A. (2020, February 13). Aquaponics Maintenance: Monitoring Water Quality. Retrieved March 20, 2020.

From
https://gogreenaquaponics.com/blogs/news

Aquapona (2019, November 21). Best Fish for Aquaponics – what's right for you. Retrieved March 20, 2020.

From https://aquapona.co.uk/best-fish-for-aquaponics/

AquaGrove (2019, December 12). The New Aquaponics. Retrieved March 20, 2020.

From
http://www.aquagrove.com/aquaponics.php

UK Survival Guides (2019, April 13). Best Fish For Aquaponics. Retrieved March 20, 2020.

From https://uksurvivalguides.com/best-fish-for-aquaponics/

Suburban Farmer (2017, October 23). Hints and Tips for Planting in an Aquaponics System. Retrieved March 20, 2020.

From http://www.suburbanfarmer.com.au/hints-tips-planting-aquaponics-system/

Scott, S. (2016, February 10) Successful Aquaponic Seed Starting. Retrieved March 20, 2020.

From https://underwoodgardens.com/successful-aquaponics-seed-starting/

Endless Food Systems (2017, January 19). What To Plant & How To Grow in Aquaponics. Retrieved March 20, 2020.

From https://www.endlessfoodsystems.com/planting-growing/

Nelson And Pade (2020, February 17) Recommended Plants and Fish in Aquaponics. Retrieved March 20, 2020.

From https://aquaponics.com/recommended-plants-and-fish-in-aquaponics/

Aquaponic Gardener (2012, November 8) Breeding Fish. Retrieved March 20, 2020.

From https://aquaponicgardener.com.au/tag/breeding-fish

Brooke, N. (2019, December 19) Aquaponics Systems Design. Retrieved March 20, 2020.

From https://www.howtoaquaponic.com/designs/aquaponics-systems/

Aquaponic Life (2019, December 19) Aquaponics System Design. Retrieved March 20, 2020.

From https://aquaponiclife.org/aquaponics/plants-hydroponics/pest-control/

Aquaponics Exposed (2016, October 29) Natural Pest Control In Aquaponics. Retrieved March 20, 2020.

From https://aquaponicsexposed.com/natural-pest-control-in-aquaponics/

MT Aquaponics (2015, May 03) Daily Operation Of My Aquaponics System. Retrieved March 20, 2020.

From http://www.mt-aquaponics.us/daily-operation-of-my-aquaponics-system/

Storey, N. (2015, May 10). Solids Removal In Aquaponics. Retrieved March 20, 2020.

From http://blog.zipgrow.com/solids-removal-in-aquaponics/

Practical Fish Keeping (2019, April 17) Why Are Aquaponics So Slow To Take Hold? Retrieved March 20, 2020.

From https://www.practicalfishkeeping.co.uk/fishkeeping-news/why-are-aquaponics-so-slow-to-take-hold

The Chefs Gardener (2020, February 10) Aquaponics Or Hydroponics. Retrieved March 20, 2020.

From https://www.thechefsgardener.com/diy-aquaponics-hydroponics/

Editorial Staff (2019, May 17) 20+ Common Mistakes People Make In Aquaponics And How To Fix Them. Retrieved March 20, 2020.

From https://www.leaffin.com/mistakes-aquaponics-guideline/

Suburban Farmer (2017, October 23) Top 5 Aquaponic Fails. Retrieved March 20, 2020.

From http://www.suburbanfarmer.com.au/top-5-aquaponics-fails/

Rowe, L. (2020, January 15) Top 12 Mistakes in Aquaponics Systems And To How to Avoid them. Retrieved March 20, 2020.

From https://aquaponicworld.com/2020/01/15/top-12-

mistakes-in-aquaponics-systems-how-to-avoid-them/

Bernstein, S. (2015, August 01) Aquaponic Worms FAQ. Retrieved March 20, 2020.

From https://www.maximumyield.com/aquaponic-worms-faq/2/1164

Fulton, C. (2020, January 25) How To Use Worms For Aquaponics (The Right Way). Retrieved March 20, 2020.

From https://helpyourpond.com/worms-for-aquaponics/

Vinje, E. (2018, May 15) How to Start an Aquaponic System (Design And Setup). Retrieved March 20, 2020.

From https://www.planetnatural.com/aquaponics/

Origin Hydroponics (2019, June 17) What's The Difference: Hydroponics Vs. Aquaponics Vs. Aeroponics. Retrieved March 20, 2020.

From
https://originhydroponics.com/hydroponics-vs-aquaponics-vs-aeroponics/

Aquaponics Commercial Backyard (2013, August 21) Aquaponics Worms. Retrieved March 20, 2020.

From https://aquaponics-commercial-backyard.blogspot.com/2013/08/aquaponics-worms.html

Brook, R. (2020, January 18) What To Consider When Choosing Fish For Aquaponics. Retrieved March 20, 2020.

From
https://homeaquaponicssystem.com/fish/consider-choosing-fish-aquaponics/

Eco Films (2012, January 08) Aquaponics And Filtration. Retrieved March 20, 2020.

From http://www.ecofilms.com.au/aquaponics-and-filtration/

The Aquaponics Source (2018, January 18) Aquaponics How-To Guide: Why Aquaponics and What Type of System? Retrieved March 20, 2020.

From https://www.theaquaponicsource.com/aquaponics-how-to-guide-why-aquaponics-and-what-type-of-system/

Backyard Aquaponics (2010, October 02) Plants. Retrieved March 20, 2020.

From http://www.backyardaquaponics.com/guide-to-aquaponics/plants/

(2012, August 19) Farming With Aquaponics. Retrieved March 20, 2020.

From https://steemit.com/gardening/@brandonv111/farming-with-aquaponics-growing-fish-and-vegetables-together

Backyard Aquaponics (2010, October 02) Plants. Retrieved March 20, 2020.

From https://www.backyardaquaponics.com/guide-to-aquaponics/running-system/

The Aquaponic Source (2013, August 05) Feeding Your Food, Plant Nutrient Deficiency And Toxicity. Retrieved March 20, 2020.

From https://www.theaquaponicsource.com/feeding-your-food-plant-nutrient-deficiency-and-toxicity-in-aquaponics-systems/

The Aquaponic Source (2013, August 21) Aquaponics And The Wonderful Worm. Retrieved March 20, 2020.

From https://www.theaquaponicsource.com/aquaponics-and-the-wonderful-worm/

On Aquaponics (2015, August 15) How To Make Your Aquaponic Plants Grow Healthily. Retrieved March 20, 2020.

From https://www.onaquaponics.com/plants-for-aquaponics

The Aquarium Adviser (2019, June 21)
Aquaponics And Bacteria. Retrieved March 20,
2020.

From
https://theaquariumadviser.com/aquaponics-and-bacteria/

Huntington, J. (2020, January 19) Nitrate Build
UP, Too Much Of A Good Thing. Retrieved
March 20, 2020.

From
https://www.aquasprouts.com/blogs/everything-aquaponics/nitrate-buildup-too-much-of-a-good-thing#

Gashgari, R., Alharbi, K., Mughrbil, K., Jan, A., &
Glolam, A. (2018). Comparison between Growing
Plants in Hydroponic System and Soil Based
System. *Proceedings of the 4th World Congress on
Mechanical, Chemical, and Material Engineering.*
https://doi.org/10.11159/icmie18.131